STRIKING IT RICH

STRIKING IT RICH

◇

Craig Vetter

William Morrow and Company, Inc.
New York

Library of Congress Cataloging-in-Publication Data

Vetter, Craig.
      Striking it rich / Craig Vetter.
        p.   cm.
      ISBN 0-688-10609-9
      1. Petroleum workers—Wyoming.   2. Petroleum industry and trade—
Wyoming. I. Title.
      HD8039.P42U68193   1991
      338.2'7282'09787--dc20   90-24131
                                                    CIP

Printed in the United States of America

First Edition

1 2 3 4 5 6 7 8 9 10

BOOK DESIGN BY M.C. DEMAIO

For Beatle and Pete

STRIKING IT RICH

1

Suzanne stood in front of the greenhouse, waving me down the long dirt drive, sobbing a little too pathetically, I thought, as if there were a lot more good-bye to the moment for her than for me.

I gave her a stiff thumbs-up, which meant, Come on now, we've talked this over, this is not as desperate as it seems—something I was trying very hard to believe that June morning as I pointed the Ford Maverick east out of the hills of northern California toward Wyoming.

I had the old car loaded with gear enough for a month, and I'd fitted it out so that I could park it on the side of the road and make at least a rat's life around it if I had to, which I expected I might, because the town I had marked on my map was famous already for the mean squeeze that had fallen on it since the oil companies had been turned loose on the land a couple of years before. Westin. Nowhere, really: a hundred empty miles beyond Salt Lake City, a hundred short of Rock Springs, out there all of a sudden with so many jobs—they said—that any man who arrived walking upright and swinging two good arms was assumed to be looking for work and was immediately hustled off the pavement into the crew cab of a pickup truck and put to work roughnecking for oil.

I figured I might have to sleep in a ditch for a while, because there are never any beds for rent in a place where jobs hunt the man, and if there are, you know they're going to cost like New York City along with everything else in town from beer to bacon and eggs. But I had that covered, too. In the trunk of the Maverick, along with my big boots, my one-burner stove, my mummy-style tent, and the sheath knife I'd worn as a Boy Scout, I had a little office that included a notebook, a dictionary, an Olivetti in a leatherette case, and a cardboard accordion file with my last nine hundred dollars stuffed into the pocket marked *M*.

The first few hours on the road were full of the high, bold spirits that always ride with you while you're clipping along just over the speed limit, and once I got myself onto U.S. 80, it was as if I'd dropped into a big river where there was nothing to do but hold myself in the current, think my thoughts, and watch the banks for something strange or interesting.

The good feeling stayed with me across the San Joaquin Valley, and up into the Sierra over Donner Pass. Then, almost exactly as I came down out of the mountains and crossed into Nevada, the bravado began to leak out of my mood. I hate Nevada. I know that just below the scrubby face of this desert beats a complex ecology no less beautiful in its way than the cool green business that goes on in the tide pools of the Pacific, but I don't care. The whole damn state reminds me of death, with its tumbleweeds, and barbed-wire fences, and telephone poles, and collapsed shacks, and everything else, as far as you can see in every direction, looking like the bones of whatever it was when it was alive. In fact, I have always thought of Nevada as the reason the Donner party pushed on into the mountains, and I have always imagined those poor doomed souls sitting around in the snow, eating each other's shoes, telling themselves, "At least Nevada's behind us."

The signs along the empty desert highway say that it is patrolled by aircraft, but the only real air traffic I have ever seen out here are the vultures and crows and magpies who hunt the hot pavement for whatever vermin have ended their miserable lives as roadmeat. You'd think the carrion eaters would make a better living off this grim trail than anybody except maybe the bandits who own the gas stations, but evidently even the scavengers have bad days out here: About sixty miles east of Reno I saw a magpie standing in the divider using all his neck muscles trying to get a chaw off the ragged edge of a blown truck tire.

Somewhere about halfway between Battle Mountain and Winnamucca, I passed a U-rent truck that had left the westbound lanes for a rest in the median, and from the look of things it had all happened pretty fast. The skid marks veered out of the slow lane, across the passing lane, then turned to a gouge where the dirt divider began, and ended where the truck lay on its roof, wheels up. The cab was in almost-perfect shape. The windshield was unbroken, the windows all rolled up as if the driver had parked it upside down and gone off somewhere looking for a cup of coffee. The cargo box hadn't done as well: It had the look of a carton that had been dropped from a great height —walls bowed, seams split—with most of someone's worldly baggage lying in a swath behind it. I slowed, but didn't stop. The scene was abandoned. There were no birds overhead.

I couldn't tell exactly what had spilled the truck, but I had some guesses. Could have been that one of those triple-trailer trucks that terrorize this road had blown by at seventy-five miles an hour and sucked the little U-rent in one side and out the other of the murderous slipstream bubble in its wake. Or maybe the road itself had spit the truck out. The right-hand lane of old 80 those days had two furrows in it that were several inches deep, and as long as you stayed in them, you could just about take your hands off the wheel and let the car steer itself. Just about. But if you hit a rut, or the bones of a rabbit, or if your attention wandered at the wrong moment so that your wheels rode up out of the grooves, it was like being shot from a sling. It had happened to me just outside of Lovelock, and before I could do anything about it, I had two wheels on the desert and two wheels on the road at seventy miles an hour, and for a quarter of a mile it was a toss-up which was going to have me.

For an hour after I passed the dead truck, I tried to keep it from turning to metaphor on me, but I couldn't do it. Seeing somebody's whole kit lying around the desert like that finally nagged me into my first small failure of nerve, and set me to reviewing my plan and my motive, neither of which was going to take much inspection.

The plan was simple, maybe even stupid: Get yourself to the roaringest boomtown in the overthrust belt and, just for a change, earn a little steady money. The motive was even simpler: For fifteen years I had been sitting over the alphabet trying to pick out interesting combinations to sell off to popular magazines, and although I had published a bunch over that time, I was broke, always broke, and in debt to my teeth, which were beginning to rot. It's a very old story, I know, older than *Beowulf,* and I'm not going to take you through it again, except to say that the whole grinding scramble had ruined my personality as well as my teeth, and that my wife—a beautiful woman ten years younger than I, whose life had yet to put a line on her face—was about sick to death of living with me. Suzanne

rarely said anything about it, but I could tell by her sighs
when she collected the dirty clothes at the end of a week
and got only a coffee-stained bathrobe from me that she
believed I was giving in to whatever struggle I had invented
for myself. Nobody asked anybody to leave, but the idea
of my going away for a while to actually earn a string of
paychecks was met with a telltale sort of enthusiasm.

When I told her it was the oil field I was thinking
about, she said, "You're kidding." When I said I was serious
and asked her why not?, she said, "I just can't picture you
with the kind of guys who do that."

I got something of the same reaction from an editor
friend who called. He was out of work and said he understood the part about being broke, "But, Jesus," he said,
"the oil patch eats people who *know* what they're doing.
Big, hairy people."

I told him I was tired of living in my head, tired of
being the mayor of a broken old chair.

"Be careful you don't change it for a wheelchair," he
said.

But if it seemed a little reckless to others that I would
strike out for the oil fields at thirty-nine years old with no
more mechanical skills than it takes to use a typewriter
badly, with no better notion of life in a boomtown than
I'd got from Mark Twain and Jack London, I just tried
not to think about it much. Instead, I thought about the
money that was out there to be made for just plain good
honest hard work. A thousand bucks a week, the grapevine
said, and you won't need a union card or any experience
beyond what it takes to stoop down and snatch a length of
pipe from here to there. If things went well, I figured I'd
have a job in a week, my debts paid in two–three months,
and be flush by the time the first snow flew.

Or else—that truck—the whole thing just might break
every important bone in my body, spit me out, and leave

me wheels-up to watch the magpies and crows and turkey vultures gather slowly overhead. And what the hell if it does, I told myself out there in the dead middle of Nevada. You can always go back to writing. In fact, if the whole experience does turn out to be a true Garden of Agony, you might even have a book.

I came out of Nevada at Wendover, scudded under a low storm front and out onto the flat white empty shallows of the Great Salt Lake. The big Mormon city came into sight on the western slope of the Wasatch. From a distance, Salt Lake is one of the best-looking cities anywhere, hugging the steep blue face of these mountains the way it does. But by the time you are close enough to read it building by building from the beat-up freeways that cut over and through the place, it isn't much to stop for, and I didn't.

I'd been on the road for fourteen hours and I should have been tired, but I wasn't feeling it because the map said that Westin was less than a hundred miles down the other side of the mountain. Even without a map, I might have known that I was getting close by the traffic that came onto the road with me just past downtown. The pickup trucks that blew past me began to have oil-company stickers on their doors, Wyoming plates on their cast-metal bumpers, and the long, slow flatbed trucks I passed were hauling bulldozers, backhoes, and the tin shells of mobile homes flapping with Wide Load banners.

The clouds were lower and darker on the pass, but it was warm, and as I started down, I opened the windows to catch the smell of the aspens and firs. Forty minutes later I crossed into Wyoming; the last of the mountain canyons gave out onto the round, squat hillscape of the prairie; the trees went off the land as if someone had poisoned it; and I picked up Westin on my radio: a cowboy voice singing about adultery and a shooting.

The wind came up and blew hard across the highway. A dust devil fifty feet high pulled itself together and moved along off to my right as if it were feeding. Then, without a sputter or a sprinkle, it started to rain in sheets and curtains. For a while I couldn't see a thing beyond twenty-five feet, and when the big trucks went by, I couldn't see my hood ornament. Then a derrick jumped into sight on a little hillock not twenty feet off the right side of the road, then another on the left, and just beyond that, buildings, a motel maybe, some gas stations. A sign said WESTIN NEXT TWO EXITS, but wherever the first one was I missed it, and for the next mile I caught glimpses only, through the heavy rain, of a little river valley and the town that spread up and down the hills around it.

I found the second off-ramp and followed a lazy circle back under the highway onto a straight two-lane road that began with several gas stations and a couple of motels, both of which had their No Vacancy signs lit. A double trailer turned left across my lane; and when I hit the brakes, a huge tanker hissed and shuddered and almost rear-ended me. From then on I was running among traffic that dwarfed me: long flatbeds full of pipe, bobtails with welding outfits on the back, water trucks, cement trucks, all of them going as if they were late for something, blowing thick sheets of water out of their wheel wells all over me and the Maverick.

I made a desperate left into the parking lot of a grungy cabin-style motel that was attached to a drive-up liquor store, bar, and roadhouse diner called the Broken Wheel. I parked, locked the doors on my way out, checked them, then made a crooked run around the puddles for the restaurant.

Inside, I bought a newspaper from a bored woman in her sixties who was leaning on a glass case full of turquoise jewelry and stomach mints. Only one of the chrome-pipe stools at the counter was empty and I took it, next to a fat boy who was whining at the waitress.

"I hope that hamburger's ready pretty soon," he said as she poured my coffee. "My stomach hurts. Why don't you go ahead and check with the cook, ask him if it's done."

The waitress left without looking at him, and he turned to me. He looked about twelve. "I hope you're not as hungry as I am," he said, "'cause they sure don't give good service in here. I should have asked for her to bring my Pepsi. I haven't eaten since this morning." He looked at the clock above the pie case. It said COORS across the face. "That's almost ten hours."

The men along the counter were looking up from their coffees and sandwiches at the kid. Only the old man next to him seemed undisturbed by the boy's fidgeting. He had the tired, beaten face of a hard drinker, but he wasn't drunk. He was hunched over a piece of paper with a pen.

"You sure are wet," said the boy as I opened my paper.

"It's raining," I told him.

"I know it's raining," he said. "It almost blowed us off the road." Then he saw the waitress through the porthole in the kitchen door. "It's coming," he said. "Here it comes . . . oh no. That's all the French fries you get with the deluxe?" He shoved his silverware out of the way and took the plate out of the waitress's hands. "Two pickle chips?" He picked the small, dark pattie off the bun and started to say something else.

"Don't tell me," said the waitress. "Mustard and catsup."

"And mayonnaise," said the kid. "Plus you forgot my Diet Pepsi."

A guy in a cowboy hat at the end of the counter chuckled, and on her way past him the waitress leaned over and said, "You be careful. *You* I can pour coffee on."

I skipped a front-page story about a helicopter crash

and went straight to the classified ads. I found "Help Wanted" behind four pages of real estate and trailer sales. There were only about fifteen notices—baby-sitter, my home...desk clerk Mesa Inn, apply in person...maid work, top wages...mobile-home sales, qualified personnel—nothing that had anything in particular to do with oil. Under "Rooms for Rent" there was a lone ad: *Furnished rooms, $50 a week.* The price was much too good to be true, which meant the truth was going to be ugly, but I circled the number anyway, because every motel I'd seen was full, and if the rain kept up, it was going to be miserable sleeping outside.

"I know you're looking for work, too, aren't you?" said the fat boy. His plate was clean enough to go right back on the shelf. "My grandad's looking for work." He pointed to the old man next to him. "He might just work here, 'cause they need a dishwasher. That's his application he's making out."

The old man gave me a shy smile. I smiled back and wondered what in the hell awful chain of fate had put him and the boy on the road together.

"Ma'am," said the boy, "my grandad's got the application all filled up."

The woman behind the cash register walked to the counter and took the form from the old man. "You're from Michigan?" she said.

"Detroit," said the old man.

"Is there someplace in town we can get ahold of you?" she asked.

"We're living in the car," said the boy. "It's a Buick. Grampa used to make Buicks."

The rain had stopped by the time I got back outside. The clouds had lifted some and lost their smudge, and the wind was down. I took the paper to a phone shell that was tacked to the building near the drive-up liquor window. I dialed the fifty-dollar rooms and got a busy signal.

"Any luck?" said somebody behind me as I hung up. When I turned, I saw a small man, maybe thirty, with a thin, hawky nose that barely separated his eyes. He was standing next to a new pickup that had a pump jack painted on the door. He had both hands in the pockets of a blue parka, and though his truck was filthy, his white jeans were perfectly white.

I told him I was getting a busy signal on a room for rent, and he said that line could be busy for a real long time in this town. I said I hadn't expected there'd be many rooms. He said there were none, not a thing he knew of. When I asked him about a place to pitch a tent, he said there were none of those, either.

"Camp in town, the cops will get ya," he said. The look on his face was a lot cockier than it was friendly. "Camp outside town, one of the ranchers probably shoot your ass."

I told him that would definitely wreck my sleep, and when he didn't smile past the pissy half-version that was already on his face, I said thanks anyway and turned for my car wondering who the hell had hired him to stand there in his cowboy boots and corp cap playing troll. When I was a couple of steps away, he asked me if I was looking for work.

"I'm looking for a drilling job," I said. "What's chances?"

"Pretty damn good if you're a driller," he said. His tone had changed, and some of the distance had gone out of his expression. The word *driller* had done it, and I knew I'd made a mistake as soon as it came out of my mouth. A driller is the man who runs the rig. *Worm* was the oil slang for the job I wanted.

"I'm not a driller," I said. "I'm a worm."

The interest went out of his face. He asked me if I

had any experience, and when I told him no, he said, "You ain't *even* a worm then, are you?"

I said something about being willing to learn, and he said everybody was willing in Westin, which just about got us back to the place where I was walking away. But I couldn't quite let it go.

"If there's no jobs, and no place to stay, you ought to just close the roads," I said. "You could pull your truck out there, get a couple of flares..."

"I didn't say there was no jobs."

"For a guy like me?"

"Depends how attached you are to that beard you're wearing." I asked what difference that made.

"Nobody's gonna hire you with that thing hanging on your face, 'cause they're using gellulite around here, and if something goes wrong and you're standing there with whiskers, it'll likely burn your face off." Now he smiled a real smile.

I didn't know what gellulite was and I didn't ask, because I wanted to be done with this man. "You know of a particular job for me?" I asked him.

He looked me in the eye, skipped a beat, then said, "Nope."

I drove out of the lot wondering whether I'd almost gotten a job or my butt kicked. He'd called me over in the first place as if he were procuring for somebody, and for just a moment I'd thought maybe the stories about getting hired right off the street were going to turn out to be true. All in all, though, the whole thing left me feeling as if I'd just dealt with a pimp who was independently wealthy.

About a quarter of a mile toward town from the diner, I turned out of the traffic onto a rutty drive that looped in and out of a couple of grassy acres. A metal sign full of bullet holes said it was the city park. Road fatigue was beginning to melt me down, and I wanted someplace to sit and relax so I could give myself the little speech about what tough people do when the going gets tough: when there are no rooms on a rainy evening in a town full of dump trucks and oil wells, where the first man you talk to mentions the possibility of having the beard blown off your face.

I pulled onto the side of the drive and stopped behind two large black road cycles that were dressed with fairings and saddlebags. A man in a rubber suit and crash helmet was standing next to one of them, reading a map and drinking coffee out of a Thermos. A woman in a matching suit joined him from the direction of a raunchy little brick building that was the bathrooms.

"David, I can't sit down in there," she told him in a tone that said they had been on the road all day. "Just to walk in made me want to puke."

"What do you want me to do about it?" he said. "I told you to piss when we got gas at Little America." Then he said, "We can't camp here anyway," and pointed to another metal sign that had also been peppered with small-arms fire: No overnight camping, no dogs, no alcoholic beverages, no open fires, no loitering, closed at sunset. Just behind the sign, a guy in a sleeveless T-shirt with tattoos up and down his arms was picking through a dumpster for food. When he found something good, he stuffed it into a black garbage bag.

I started with the front page of the paper this time and got about halfway through a story that said the city administrator was optimistic that the town would be able to stop pumping raw sewage into the Thicket River by August, when there was a knock on the roof of the Maverick. I ducked, and when I looked up, I saw a long-haired kid in an army fatigue jacket that was too big for him. He was smiling and holding up an old backpack as if he'd just shot it.

"Didn't mean to make you jump," he said when I rolled the window down. "I was just wondering if you'd like to buy some weed? Very good shit. Grown by hippies in Oregon."

I told him I had plenty.

"What kind?" he said.

"Grown in California by hoodlums," I told him.

"It's not sensimilla, is it?"

I nodded that it was. "You want to sell some?" he asked.

When I told him no, he said, "What the hell, let's get high," and because I could find no real larceny in his young eyes, I said sure and let him in the passenger door.

"California," he said as he sat. "You from there?"

When I said yes, he told me that he'd lived in San Jose for six months, then moved back to Portland, where he'd grown up. "You want to smoke this garbage I got, or how 'bout some of your shit?" he said. I looked at him. "I'm not trying to hustle you, I'm not," he said. "I'll give you some of mine—here—I'd just like a toke or two of the good stuff, you know."

I got a film can out of my dop kit and handed it to him. He sniffed into it as if it were brandy, then got about the same look on his face as the fat kid when his hamburger was served. He took some papers out of his pocket and started to roll.

"You working in town?" I asked.

"Hell, no way," he said. "I'm outta here just as soon as I get my van running—tonight, I hope—I'm gone. I been in this shithole for seven days, and it seems like about seven months. Couldn't get a job, cops wouldn't let me sleep in my van, haven't had a shower since I been here, haven't even *talked* to a woman, and yesterday I was parked over at the Big Eighty truck stop and some sombitch stole every tool I own, which is worth about twenty-five-hundred dollars. I take these things as a sign."

"I thought there was plenty of work around here?" I said. He took a deep drag off the joint, held it, then talked the smoke out of his lungs.

"There might be, probably is, 'cept I'm a carpenter, and there ain't much of that around here. You'd think there would be. Big oil boom, right? You'd think they was building a town, but they ain't. They're trucking it in. All that aluminum shit. Couple of winos with staple guns can put one of those jobs together in a half hour. Since I been here, I had exactly one job offered to me. Some old lady in town wanted me to fix up a chicken coop in her backyard so she could rent it out for two hundred dollars a month, no toilet, no water. Two hundred a month, and she'll probably get it, too. She wanted to give me eight bucks an hour for the job, two, three days' work, which would have been okay except she wanted me to kill the godamn chickens ... with my Skilsaw or something; I don't know. There was about twenty of them pecking around the yard."

He gave me the joint and asked if I was looking for a job.

"On a rig," I told him.

"Oh, you can have that," he said. "I mean, there's probably plenty of those jobs around, but you couldn't get me on a oil rig for nothing. In the first place, I hate big machines. I can't stand all that steel around me. I like wood, that's all. You can *work* with wood. Smells good, feels good when you grab it. Grab an I-beam sometime—see what I mean? No soul. And I'll tell you something else. I don't even like the type of person who works on the rigs. Remind me of the guys who took metal shop in high school—you know the guys? Give themselves tattoos with ice picks, made their first zip guns by the time they was thirteen. Tough guys. This town's full of tough guys, and they're a pain in the ass."

"I think I just met one," I said.

"You're going to meet a lot more, you hang around this town too long."

"I need the money," I told him. "I've been broke for a very long time."

"Yeah, the money's good," he said. "But I knew a guy from Portland went over to Gillette for about six months, and he made him some big bucks, for sure, except that when he got home, he had to spend 'em with his left hand because he got his right one pinched off in some kind of goddamn pipe claw."

"Don't tell me that," I said. "I've been here an hour, and you're the second guy who's done that to me. I'm trying to hold on to a positive attitude going into this thing, and ..."

"You mean you never done it before?"

I looked at him in a way that meant, Give me a break.

"I ain't saying nothing," he said. "You gotta start somewhere, and you're probably better off not knowing anything. I mean, you'll probably be real careful." He dragged on the joint again. "You take metal shop?" He was smiling.

"One semester, junior high school."

"Well, that's good," he said. "You made the little tin box, right? Gave it to your mom to keep her hairpins in? ... I'm not trying to scare you off this thing, really I'm not. I mean, you'll probably make a shitload of money, go home, buy a bunch of cocaine for all your friends and tell 'em stories that'll make their hair stand straight up on their heads. You married?"

I nodded.

"You trust her?"

"Trust her for what?" I said as if I didn't understand the question.

"Guess that's a little personal," he said. "Sorry. Just thinking about my own situation is all. My wife isn't too good at being alone. Most women ain't." He burned his fingers on the last of the joint, then put the roach in his pocket. "I feel like I smoked most of that myself, didn't I?" he said.

I told him it was okay, that I still had to find a place to camp, that I didn't want to get too stupid before then. I asked him if he knew a spot.

"There's Dead Horse Canyon," he said. "About six miles out of town. But the road is real bad dirt, and I don't even know if this old buggy of yours would make it. I don't think you'd want to anyway, because, I mean, it's *Grapes of Wrath* out there. Bunch of mean hobo types living in the back of their pickup trucks. I do know another place, though. Right here in town. I've been using it myself for the last three nights, but since I am definitely outta here tonight, no matter what, I'll be happy to pass it on to you. It doesn't smell too good, but it's got four walls and a roof, and you can't smell anything when you're asleep anyway."

"It's not that chicken coop?" I said.

"Hell no. This place is free. Tell you what: You drive me across town to the Big Eighty and give me a jump to get my van going—my battery has about had it—I'll show you the place on the way over."

As we pulled out, he said, "Now the smell *is* bad, but there are absolutely no other hassles. Cops don't even know about it. Too obvious, that's why. Right under their noses."

Traffic had thinned, but almost immediately as I pulled out of the park, I got an anxious pickup on my bumper. It was a big Ford that sat so high over the road all I could see of it in my mirror was half the grille work and a little set of hooded foglights. It made me feel small and slow again, and when it swung out to pass, the feeling got worse, because in the bed of the truck—as if to say you ought to see my big brother—was a tire that probably weighed a thousand pounds, that could have seated thirty people for dinner if you'd put legs on it.

The carpenter pointed ahead of us and to the right. "We're coming up on your place," he said.

I was looking for what he was talking about, but all I could see was the rodeo grounds. A whitewashed facade thirty feet high stood at the edge of the road and was hung with a banner advertising Cowboy Days.

"Where?"

"Right through there," he said, pointing to an entrance tunnel that ran under the bleachers to the dirt oval that was the arena.

"Don't stop," he said. "You can check it out after dark. There's this hot-dog stand built in the tunnel there under the seats. Lock's busted. All you got to do is get over that Cyclone fence without anybody seeing you."

It looked doubtful to me, but I didn't say anything. The carpenter seemed very proud of the place, it was starting to sprinkle again, and even the dumpiest of the motels we were passing had their little No signs lit.

The road curved left past a well service company, then crossed a two-lane bridge over the Thicket River. A pretty scattering of old brick buildings came into view among the trees on a low hillside. Westin had been a nice little town before oil, I thought. Out my window was a mill yard that had huge logs piled for a quarter of a mile in every direction around the base of a high, cone-shaped furnace that was laying white smoke in a flat cloud along the river, down the valley.

We followed the pickup with the big tire through a short tunnel under the railroad tracks. The carpenter called it the rabbit hole, and said that every scrap of cross-town traffic had to squeeze through it, and that during the morning and evening shift change it took a half an hour to go half a mile.

Just out the other side we turned right onto Station Street, and the carpenter began a narrative that lasted three blocks and included a shooting he almost witnessed at the Ranger Bar, a fist fight he heard about between two women in front of the bus station, and an empty whiskey bottle he'd actually seen dropped out of the third story of the old Simms Hotel onto a cowboy's head. All the buildings here were brick or stone, but whatever businesses they'd housed when this was the proud face of the town were mostly gone now, replaced by video parlors, T-shirt shops, a couple of dingy cafés, and an antique store. We turned left at Jessup's Hardware onto a long, straight boulevard that ran for a mile up a gradual hill under hundred-year elms, past solid old houses with big porches whose lawns and gardens sloped down to high curbs.

"Looks like they used to have work for carpenters around here," I said.

" 'Bout the time they drove the golden spike," said the kid. "That wasn't far from here, you know. I was talking to some old guy said his daddy was there for that. Probably like the Super Bowl, though. Everybody *says* they was there."

At the top of the hill the street bent right, flattened, the trees quit, and the houses gave way to an ugly strip of motels, gas stations, and quick-stop groceries that sat parking lot to parking lot for a quarter of a mile.

"Big Eighty's up there on the right next to the Mesa Inn," the carpenter said. "My van's on the back edge of the place."

We followed a cattle truck slowly through the rows of cars and motor homes that were parked around the coffee shop and road store in the middle of the property, then out toward fifty or sixty big rigs that sat in almost perfect rank where the asphalt turned to dirt.

"There it is," he said. "That beautiful old green piece of shit Dodge over there next to the Peterbilt. At least it's still here."

I parked so that we could reach his battery from mine, and he got into the back of the van to rummage for his jumper cables. When he found them tangled on themselves, he came around to the open hood of the Maverick and said, "Who is it, I wonder, who goes around the world tying knots in everything that has two ends? Did you ever wonder about that, or am I just stoned? I mean, the last time I put these cables in here, they were in a neat coil, and now there are like six perfect Boy Scout knots in it. Look at this mess. It's like when nobody's looking, these things are alive and squirming; then when you need 'em, they play dead."

I told him he was stoned, but right. Then I said something about the secret life of inanimate things.

"And you notice," he said, "that if you put something away with a bunch of knots already in it, nobody ever sneaks in and unties any of them."

I started the Maverick and hooked the cable to my battery. Then the carpenter opened the hood of the van, and the philosophical mood died a quick death.

"You gotta be shitting me," he said, looking down into his engine. "I don't fucking believe it. My battery's gone. They stole a goddamn dead battery. I swear to God I don't believe this town."

The clamps blew sparks as he threw the cable down. I unhooked my end and said, "You can probably get another one here at Big Eighty."

"You're goddamn right I can," he said, "and it's just about dark enough."

"I meant you could probably buy one."

"*You* could probably buy one," he said. "Not me, god-damnit. I got just enough money for gas and burgers between here and Portland, and I'm getting out of this shithole town tonight, I don't care what. It's about time to start doing unto others around here."

I told him he was on his own and thanked him for the tip about the rodeo grounds.

"They stole a goddamn dead battery," he said again, but he was talking into the engine well of the van, not to me.

I started to get back into the Maverick, then decided I might as well make another call about the room to rent. "I'm going to use the phone over here," I said. "Good luck on the road."

"Hey, thanks anyway," he said as I started across the parking lot toward the coffee shop. "Hope you strike it rich."

There were three pay phones just inside the front doors of the little restaurant. Two of them had napkin notes that said OUT OF ORDER pasted over the coin slots. A short man with a paunch was arguing into the one that worked.

Early dark fell while I waited. I imagined the carpenter somewhere out there in the drizzle duck-walking among the cars and trucks, a pirate with a wrench in his mouth, shopping for the battery that was going to get him to Oregon. His tales of Westin hadn't exactly relaxed me, but they hadn't surprised or discouraged me, either. I didn't like the part about the friend who'd left a hand on the rig up in Gillette, but people always tell you the worst of what they know about everything, and I wasn't going to dwell on it. I'd expected the place I was looking for to be full of thieves and short on rooms, although I hadn't expected the pinch to reach down far enough to evict the town's chickens because they couldn't lay fast enough to keep up with the rent. Still, I'd only been in town a couple of hours, and already the carpenter had made me a gift of his secret roof, which seemed to argue that even in the chaos and greed of a boomtown, a loose, accidental sort of a brotherhood was possible. And I liked the carpenter. If only for the fact that he wouldn't go after those chickens with his power tools.

There were two people in line behind me by the time the trucker finished his call, but mine didn't take long. Room for rent was still busy, and I decided to let it go till morning.

The rain was small but steady when I crossed back through the parking lot. My long day was overcoming the exhilaration of arrival, and I knew I was going to have to check out the rodeo grounds and lie down there or somewhere else before long. I could have slept in the Maverick; but the way I had it packed, there wasn't going to be much rest to it if I did. And I wanted to try out my tent anyway. There was no telling how long I was going to have to sleep on the ground before I found a bed, and I wanted to get used to it.

The carpenter had evidently found himself an easy mark, because the van was gone when I got to the Maverick. I pictured him twenty miles on his way to Salt Lake; and some poor fool in the restaurant eating a nice chicken-fried steak that was going to cost him a lot more than he thought. I chuckled to myself and started my car, or anyway, turned the key to start my car, and when there wasn't so much as a click, I felt a tingle up the back of my head and a line from John Donne translated itself out of poetry and hung there for me. "It's you, sucker" was the gist of it. I turned the key twice more, as if wishes were electricity, then just sat there in the dark with rain falling on the roof.

You bastard, I thought. You rathead, thieving bastard. Didn't even have the guts to kill a chicken, and you steal my battery.

I got the hood up, and where the battery should have been was a socket wrench, which I took as the carpenter's apology, his invitation for me to join the chain of larceny, and I might have if I were a little better with my hands. As it was, instead of going under somebody else's hood, I went into my own trunk, into the accordion file, got a hundred dollars out of the pocket marked *M,* and went looking to buy six volts.

The kid who was working the pumps at the Big 80 said they didn't have any batteries at all. The teenager at the Standard station across the street climbed a ladder, read the boxes on a high shelf, then came down saying yeah, he had one. He checked a book with plastic pages and said it would be eighty-five dollars. I said, what?, and he put his finger on the amount and repeated it for me. At the Shell station a block and a half up, an old man with three days' stubble told me through the glass of his bullet-proof booth that they only sold gas. Back at the Standard, the kid climbed the ladder again and this time brought down a six-volt battery that would have cost me fifty dollars anywhere else. While he added the tax, I told him this was the second time I'd been robbed that evening. Don't tell me about it, he said.

On my way back across town I checked the motels again. Their parking lots were full of pickups and Jeeps and Broncos and Blazers, and the only signs that were lit were the ones that said they were full.

There was a car parked in front of the rodeo grounds. I pulled into a dirt parking lot across the street that served three or four shops, all closed. I parked next to a lit yellow sign that sat on a little trailer. FREE SPINAL EXAM, it said over the name of a chiropractor.

From where I was sitting, I couldn't quite see whether the car was empty or not, so I watched a while. Pretty soon, a cream-colored police car cruised onto the dirt and threw a spotlight onto the rear window. Two cops got out holstering big, nasty billy sticks, and a head raised up out of the backseat into the bright light. It was the fat kid. He put his hand up to shade his eyes, then reached over the front seat. The old man sat up slowly and opened his window. While one cop talked to him, the other walked a slow circle around the car, shining a long-barreled flashlight into each window. The old man handed over a driver's license. The cop took it back to his car and used the radio. A minute later he was back with the license, and a little speech. Then he and his partner got back into the squad car and waited while the old Buick threw a long plume of dirty white smoke, then rolled slowly onto the road toward the freeway. The cops drove off toward downtown.

I waited; but I didn't want to wait too long, because I knew the cops would be back, and I didn't want my name in their little book the first night in town. I figured that once I was out of the Maverick, it would be just another parked car in a lot with several, and it didn't seem likely to draw much heat. Traffic was light—thirty seconds or a minute between cars—and while I got the rhythm of it, I gathered my tent, sleeping bag, a flashlight, and the sheath knife, which seemed a little silly. I knew damn well that if I had to fight for my little piece of shelter that night, I was going to run instead; but I told myself that if I was waving a knife, it would probably slow whoever was chasing me.

I locked the car, and when I could see no headlights in either direction, I sprinted across the road, threw my bags over the chain-link gate into the dark of the tunnel, then scrambled and humped myself over after them. I squatted where I landed, then listened to hear if I'd vaulted into somebody else's camp. There was nothing except for the sound of water dripping through the seats. I crept a little deeper, and when I still heard nothing, I began to think that maybe the carpenter had been telling the truth when he said the place was his secret. It was for sure he hadn't lied about the smell. The dampness was driving it up out of the dirt and soaking it out of the old wooden beams. It was more than one odor, a soup of them, really, but the root stock of it had the unmistakable smell of an open-pit latrine.

About halfway through the tunnel I found a Dutch door with a padlock on it. It looked secure; but true to the carpenter's word, when I gave it a yank, it came undone. Then I opened the top half of the door, and the stink rose up two times worse, as if I had just broken the seal on the inner sanctum of some shrine that preserved the living memory of ten thousand pissing cowboys.

Not me, I thought; not tonight, not ever. A smell like that would reach into your dreams no matter how deeply you slept. Or maybe even if you were dead. I closed the door and walked out of the tunnel into the arena. It had stopped raining. The air was still and beautifully fresh. Bleachers enough for a thousand people stood on one side of the ring, and opposite them were the stock pens and chutes. The bottom of the chutes was a muddy collection of hoof-sized puddles, but behind them in the holding pens the ground was covered with a litter of sawdust and manure about six inches deep. When I got the loamy mix in my hand, it was damp but not sopping, and though it smelled of animals and dirt, it didn't stink.

It took me about five minutes to pitch my New Age ground-hugger tent. I put my bag inside, my boots by my head, left the rest of my clothes on, and stretched out. Somewhere a dog was barking. Now and then a piece of traffic went by behind the bleachers. The moon lit the edges of the clouds without showing itself; and on the one hillside I could see through the rail fence, a lone rig sat quietly, its derrick lit like the mast of a ship.

That's it, I thought. Tell yourself you are on the wharves of a nasty old harbor town looking for a ship to sign you on; you and the pickpockets and tattooed head-hunters; the one-eyed mates and the bushy-tailed cabin boys; the old salts who sail because they don't know anything else and the green young fools who do it because they don't know anything at all.

What the hell kind of ship would sign you on? I remember thinking just before I dropped off.

2

I woke ears first to the thumping of helicopter blades miles away. Just for a minute, I had no idea where I was. Then a huge diesel something growled past, I remembered, and everything came awake. My breath looked like a flashlight beam. The kind of light you have to catch out of the corner of your eye was just squeezing into the lower edge of the sky, but not enough to dim the stars, which were vivid. It looked as if it was going to be a nice day.

For a while I lay perfectly still. I didn't want to break the bubble of damp warmth in the sleeping bag; and, anyway, my first thoughts weren't on the day ahead. I was thinking about home, Suzanne. I wondered if she was going to remember to water the greenhouse on her way to work.

A friend and I had built the little hothouse the year before out of lumber salvaged from a Victorian remodel in San Francisco. We hammered the big old two-by-fours into a frame, then tacked on plastic panels for walls and roof. I loaded the beds with compost, planted twelve seeds from an ounce of fourth-generation California marijuana, then for eight months I watered and clipped and worried them up into beautiful green trees. Four of them dropped male sacs, and I tore them out and threw them away. Then I watched as the unfertilized females sat there like nuns, using all of their magnificent energy to make oil instead of seeds. A month before harvest the smell of the place was enough to knock you down, enough to stone the spiders, whose webs, I swear, grew careless. We took just over two pounds of greasy sensimilla out the door in October and sold most of it to a gay anesthesiologist. The rest I gave to friends and to myself.

Chances of the young crop I'd left behind coming to the same bounty seemed slim. Suzanne had her own life, a busy one that started early in the morning and went late almost every day. In the months before I left, the two of us seemed to share only the tired fringes of our days. She reported the events of her work week in broad strokes only, and listened to my reports on progress in the greenhouse without losing her place in whatever she was reading. She didn't smoke, and she didn't garden, but aside from the perfect silences she dropped into when I got going on one of my stoned rhapsodies about the horticultural miracle I was tending, she never discouraged me. In fact, the day I told her about my Wyoming plans, she volunteered to water the plants before I'd even thought about it.

"They're weeds, right?" she said. "They pretty much take care of themselves, don't they?"

Pretty much, I told her. You didn't have to watch them and groom them and just generally fall into their service the way I had. There were a couple of things they needed besides water, but I told her I'd set things up to make it as easy as possible. The day before I left,

I hung a page of garden wisdom just inside the greenhouse door. I headed it with a snippet from Virgil to reassure her that failure in the garden was no tragedy, that if the whole thing went to compost, it would be all right: "...seeds and plants, and what will thrive and rise, / And what the genius of the soil denies," it said. Below that, my prose.

Heat is the killer in here, the natural heat of summer in these hills bottled up in this greenhouse. Water these plants every other day. Turn on the drip system in the morning and leave it on for half an hour, while you make your breakfast, take your shower.

Water every day during a hot spell.

Keep the door closed and padlocked, but make sure the back window is open a crack and that the dormer windows are always open. They need air almost as much as water. Watch for the plants to droop, and if they do, hose the place down as if you were fighting a fire.

Every two weeks use the food on the shelf. Instructions on the label.

Earwigs and snails ought to be murdered summarily. All other bugs can pretty much have their way unless they get greedy. General rule: If a bug moves slowly enough to step on or pinch, do it. If it's faster than that, leave it alone because it will probably eat something slower.

Watch for the burrowers—moles and gophers—and let me know at the first sign of either. Although if they discover the place, we're probably sunk.

At the first sign of trouble from cops or thieves, tear everything out by the roots, throw it away, and put on that innocent look you are so very good at.

And touch them now and then, shake them by the stalks so they'll know you're paying attention.

At the crucial moment I intended to tell her over the phone exactly how to read the subtle difference between the males and the females, how to tell when they were ripe for the wind to do its work, to make a marriage. At that point, proximity was all it was going to take.

I lay in my bag for a minute feeling lonely, wondering why I'd ducked the carpenter's question about fidelity. Not that a thieving dirt-eater like him deserved an honest answer, or even belonged in a conversation about trust. Still ... truth was that whatever tethers of the heart were left between Suzanne and me probably weren't strong enough to trust anymore. Somehow, she had become animated by the looseness that had crept into our connection. I'd grown numb. Which made my trip ... what? A man testing an old rope by hanging his entire weight on it? Never mind, I thought as I forced myself up and out of my cocoon. The cold air jerked me back into the morning at hand. I rolled my gear, listened to the crows overhead shouting at each other, and to the rising beat of the traffic behind the bleachers.

I climbed out of the rodeo grounds over a fence into the parking lot of a motel next door where a plastic stallion, big as life, stood in the neon shine of the word *Palomino*. Lights and showers were on in about half the rooms. I jogged across the road to the Maverick, started the motor, wiped the windows, turned the heater on "blow," then sat there and shook till the worst of the chill came off. Then I drove back toward the Broken Wheel against the headlights of the traffic that was headed for the rabbit hole.

Evidently, it had been a busy night at the little bar and diner, and not everyone had gone home entirely happy. The glass door was shattered bottom to top from a point about boot high. Someone had propped it open with a news rack and hung a hand-lettered sign that said IF YOU WOULD

RATHER FIGHT THAN SWITCH BARS, YOU WILL BE 86ED. The tables inside were full. The counter was a mixed thicket of cowboy hats and corp caps over eggs and potatoes.

The woman behind the cash register was talking to an old man who had a rancher's face and clothes. He was saying, "I thought they was going to kill that nigger when he walked into the ladies' bathroom like that . . . would have killed him probably if the cops hadn't already been there on another dispute." The woman was shaking her head as if to say, This used to be a nice little town. When I got her attention, she took my Thermos, filled it with coffee, and charged me two dollars, all without taking her ears off the old man's Friday-night-at-the-Mesa-Inn story.

" 'Course, I almost never go in that bar anymore anyhow," he told her. "What with the cowboys and the oil trash, you know something stupid's gonna happen over there almost any damn night of the week."

I drove the rest of the way out to the eastern edge of town and turned onto a dirt road up the flank of a hill that looked as if it would get the first of the sun. On my way, I fished around on the radio. I hoped I might get a Salt Lake or even a Denver signal, but everything on the band except the Westin country-western station was the kind of fuzz that makes you feel a long way from anywhere.

KTRY had the regional news on, and the first item I heard was from Yellowstone, where a group of rangers had trapped a grizzly at the park dump the day before. They got her in a cage, shot her full of bear tranquilizers, and when the leader of the group—a man named Bizonni—figured she was all the way under, they dragged her out of the trap to do whatever it was they were going to. I adjusted the station and got the volume up because somehow I knew what was coming. "She came out of her stupor suddenly," said the newscaster, "and chased Mr.

Bizonni down. A brief scuffle ensued. Mr. Bizonni suffered lacerations on his hand and puncture wounds in his thigh before the bear ran off into the woods. All other members of the research team were unhurt."

Unhurt, perhaps, but not unmoved by the experience, I thought. Score one for the grizzlies, out there in those mountains, the last of the hostile natives.

I parked in a turnout near the top of the hill, turned off the motor and the lights but left the radio on. From where I sat, I had the full three-dollar-fifty-cent view: to the west up Rodeo Road, which was almost entirely awake with hardworking traffic by now; across the river and the railroad tracks, over the mill yard into the pretty heart of town, then out to the ragged freeway edge of things. To the south and east I had a look for a hundred miles over the prairie where the valleys deepened and the divided lanes of old 80 disappeared and reappeared among the hills like perfect ski tracks. Just at the limit of my sight a beautiful range of mountains broke the horizon as if it were where Wyoming ended and Colorado began.

The car steamed when the sun hit it. The hill I was on threw a clean shadow down toward the Broken Wheel, and a recorded announcement came on the radio from the Westin office of the State Job Service: A telephone voice said good morning, then listed six or eight jobs that were looking to be filled, fry cooks and night maids mostly, but there was one truck driver wanted. The voice said that all the jobs would be available at 8:00 A.M. when the office opened. I drank my coffee and tried to imagine myself wheeling around in one of the big dumpers or water trucks that were moving in and out of town below me. It was a tough mental picture to hold, but I knew that before the day was over, I was probably going to be asking for jobs a lot less likely than that one, and that I was going to have to make it sound as if I were born to the work. So I put Job Service first on the day's agenda, and decided that when the question of experience came up, I'd just go ahead and lie with all the color and detail that only years of writing for hire can develop in a man.

Before anything, I needed a shave. I had no idea whether the punk in the parking lot had told me the truth about my beard, but I hadn't seen any whiskers at the counter or tables in the Broken Wheel or on the faces that looked down on me from the truck windows, which made it seem likely that style more than explosives demanded a shiny face in Westin.

A gas station seemed to be the best place to get a sink for the job unless I wanted to squat over the cold and sewery Thicket River with my camp mirror and a box of bandages, which I didn't. I'd taken my beard off only one other time in ten years, and even with hot water it had been a massacre. I needed a gas-station lav, and finding a friendly one was going to be hard, I figured. The way they sat on the banks of the highway in the middle of a boomtown, it seemed likely that the stations in Westin had braced themselves long ago against the inundation of cross-country flotsam and jetsam that hoboed and hitchhiked through, especially in summer. I decided to try the Standard where I'd bought my battery.

There was a different teenager at the pumps when I parked near the shut service bays. He yelled over that there wasn't going to be a mechanic till ten.

"Don't need a mechanic," I told him. "I got a new battery here last night, and everything's working fine. What I'd like to do is use your bathroom to get a shave."

"Can't do that," said the kid, but his tone had "I'm sorry" in it, a plain sort of friendliness that evidently no tide of strangers could quite undo.

"I'll tell you what," I said. "It's my first day in town,

I'm looking for work, and I don't think this beard is going to go over very well around here. I just don't see too many of them, you know?"

"Just on the dirtbags," said the kid.

"That's exactly it," I said. "I'm no dirtbag, at least not in the traditional sense."

"What?" he said, and all of a sudden I knew that even if I did shave my beard, I was going to have to stop talking like that around here. I'd actually heard a man in the Broken Wheel that morning *uncorrect* his grammar: "I told him he was crazy, that they were... they was elk," he said. I sat there next to him—an English major in the oil field—admiring the way he'd undone his faux pas, wondering if my own fastidious tongue was going to keep me out of work. The kid in the gas station stood there looking at me as if I'd just taken on a foreign accent.

"What I mean is, I've been on the road, I slept on the ground last night, and I know I don't look too good, but..."

"It's nothing against you," said the kid. "I'll get run off if my boss catches me letting you use the bathroom without buying nothin'. I can't do it."

"Listen, I'll open the hood of my car, and if your boss comes, we'll tell him you were just tightening the cables of the battery I bought here last night, and I slipped into the can and you didn't see what I was doing. He's not going to be able to fire you on a deal like that, is he?"

"Yeah he will," said the kid. "He don't need no reason to send me back to the house. Anyway, all that hair's gonna clog the drain."

"No. Not a hair will go down the drain," I said. "And when I'm through, I'll clean the whole damn place, whatever's in there, not just my mess."

"Now you don't even know what you're saying."

"Doesn't matter," I told him. "This is important to me.

You won't find a hair, not one hair, not mine, not anybody's. You show me a mop, give me some rags, and I'll clean the whole place so you could take a date in there if you wanted to."

"God..." he said as if his stomach were moving on him.

"...and I'll give you five dollars. Take me less than fifteen minutes..."

"All right," he said. "But you'll have to be quick about it." When I tried to hand him a five, he said, "Nah, I don't want that. Just do it fast. I'll get the hood of your car up."

"There's no hot water," he said as he let me in.

In fact, the whole place was a shame. The urinal was jammed in the flush position, and the toilet seat was hanging by one hinge. All that was left above the sink where the mirror should have been was a shard about the size of a postcard, about the shape of Nevada. The only paper towels in the place were on the floor, which was slippery wet and full of muddy boot prints. The little ceiling fan was dead with grime, and the air smelled as if it had been brought across town from the hot-dog stand under the rodeo bleachers. Finally, it wasn't hard to understand why the kid had winced and called God's name when I suggested taking a date into the place. What was hard to imagine was that plumbing in Westin was at such a premium that this terrible little shithole was locked and guarded.

The tap was spring-loaded and turned itself off when I let go. The water was icy. There was no stopper, so I used a couple of towels off the floor to clog the drain, then I filled the bowl and stuck my face into it. I took half a step backward and ducked to get a look at my beard in the mirror, and for just a minute I thought I might leave it on. It was an old friend, after all. I looked hard, trying to imagine it gone. I was going to miss it. It filled my hollow cheeks, added weight to my weak chin, and just generally put a touch of the Old Testament to what I remembered as a sort of a musical-comedy face. To hell with these people, I thought. Let them take me with my whiskers or leave me. I'm ready to work. I'll lift and haul and pound, and I'll climb their derricks like a monkey, and when they've named something for me once, they won't have to name it again. I'm as tough as they'll ever need, and my beard comes with me. Then, just for an instant, I imagined the thing in flames, and my resolution to chop it off came back. Nobody is tough when his face is on fire.

Then, too, there was the gray. In the grimy light that was getting through the transom of the nasty little room, the shock on my left cheek and the chevron of white on my chin seemed to undo everything that was still boyish about my face. And no matter what else was true, I knew that I had come to a place of boy-men and that I would be lined up next to them before the hiring, and that thirty-nine is to twenty-one what meat loaf is to veal when you look it in the face. It was possible, of course, that the lines and scars would have deepened and matured in a way that would be worse traitor to my masquerade than the gray hairs, but I doubted it. And besides, the kid outside was jumpy, and this thing needed to be done.

I made myself a sideburn with the first two strokes, and whatever the razor didn't cut off, it tore out. I worked my way down the cheek around what was going to be a mustache and drew first blood at the corner of my mouth. But the real slashing didn't come till I got to the cleft in my chin. I had forgotten it was there. The whole awful business took about ten minutes, and when I was through, there was blood on the porcelain, and the water in the hairy little bowl was pink. I squinted at myself in the small piece of mirror. I looked a little like I'd been thrown through the window of a jeep. But if you could see past the blood and the nicks and the one gash, you were looking at a younger man. By more than a few years, I thought. It was a face with some miles on it, for sure, but they didn't add up to more than about thirty-five years. Thirty-six maybe. I smiled at myself. It hurt.

I got the roll of toilet paper off the commode, and while I was patching bits of it onto the smaller wounds, the kid came in with a mop and a rag.

"Damn," he said when I looked at him.

"Don't worry," I said. "I'll have the place cleaned up in five minutes...two minutes."

"You're all tore up," he said.

"Looks like a suicide try, doesn't it? Never mind. I have a first-aid kit in my car. Your boss isn't here, is he? Good. Then give me the mop and don't worry. I'll get the blood off things, and there won't be a hair in here."

Once I had the four small nicks plastered, I made a thick pad of toilet paper and held it against the smiling slash on my chin. After a minute or so it stuck, which gave me both hands to mop and polish and gather the debris of the place into one corner.

The kid was waiting for me outside the door. "You're gonna have to haul the trash," I told him. "But I think it looks pretty good in there."

"You might ought to get a doctor for that thing," he said. "Looks deep."

"Nah, it's all right," I said. "No arteries in the chin. Lot more vessels than you'd think though, huh? But let me ask you something." I took a step back. "Don't look at the cuts and be honest now. I want you to tell me if I look younger than I did with a beard."

"I don't know. I guess so," he said.

"How old?"

"About thirty."

"That's what I wanted to hear," I told him. "You're a good man."

"If you want to go back in there and bandage yourself up, it's okay," he said. "I got a big first-aid kit in the office."

"I can do it in the car," I said. "I have to get into town and see the people at Job Service."

"What kind of job you looking for?"

"Worm hand."

"You'll never get that at Job Service," he said. "You'd be better off hanging out in the bars."

I told him I was going to do some of that, too, thanked him again, then drove back toward the center of the old village with the sun in my eyes. The morning man on the radio was saying, "Come on Westin, get up. Let's go to work." Then he played a song called "If You Could Spend the Wages of Sin, I'd Own This Miserable Town."

I was trying not to take the kid's estimate of thirty years old too seriously. It made me feel good, made everything seem possible, but people under twenty have no eye for age. If you stood a teenager in front of the Taj Mahal and asked him when it was built, he'd probably tell you "sometime in the fifties." Still, if he thought thirty, I might get away with thirty-five. I did the math and told myself to remember when they asked that my birthday was 1947.

Job Service was on Main Street, and I parked catty-corner from it in the shadow of the old courthouse, not far from a memorial to the local soldiers who had fallen in the first Great War. It was a granite pillar, and the infantryman on top of it had his bayonet fixed. He was wearing gaiters, and one of the soup-bowl helmets of that war, and he was striking a who-goes-there pose, as if a thousand Huns were expected on this lawn before sunset. Behind him, in a pen made of chain link, sat Union Pacific number 42, a big old steam engine gone to rust, stuck, as if she were waiting for someone to drive the tracks over the hills to her cowcatcher from the west, to her coaltender from the east.

It took two Band-Aids to cover the cut on my chin, and by the time I had them fixed, there were five people on the sidewalk outside the storefront that was Job Service. Three of them were wearing full-outfit backpacks with sleeping bags and aluminum pots hanging from them. From where I was, they looked like kids, two boys and a girl. Their clothes were perfect Sears, Roebuck vagabond, from their crepe-soled boots to the bandannas they wore as hats. They were eating oranges, and the girl was collecting up the peels and putting them into a plastic bag, which made me think they were on their way to California to save the whales.

Next to them was a tall, flat-faced man in motorcycle boots, tight black pants, and a black T-shirt with the words OIL FIELD TRASH AND PROUD OF IT across the front. He was talking to an old man who was sitting comfortably on what looked to be a rolled mover's blanket. I took him to be about sixty years old. He was wearing an old flannel shirt, slacks with no knees, and blown-out sneakers that were the color of the road.

Around eight, a young man in a sport coat drew up the blinds in the plate-glass window, opened the door and, without saying anything to anyone, took a seat at his desk, which was separated from the waiting room by an elbow-high counter.

The old man sat at a cafeteria table, and I sat with him. The rest leaned on the counter. One of the boys asked if he had to fill out an application or anything. The man behind the counter said he'd be there in a minute. It was the same voice I'd heard on the radio except that the public-relations tone had been replaced by a flatter, more distant timber that seemed to mean, "Just because you can see me doesn't mean I'm available."

There were about three seats between me and the old man, but I could smell him as perfectly as if I'd been wearing his shirt. He had a benign face, and his teeth were almost black. When he set his bedroll on the floor between us, I spotted a Bible tucked under the hank of rope that tied it. We smiled at each other, and he asked for a cigarette. He tore the filter off, put the ragged end in his mouth, then lit it with a wooden match that he put back into his pocket after he'd blown it out.

I asked him if he was riding the freight trains.

"Sometimes," he said. "Just sometimes anymore. Rode one here from Salt Lake last night, but that's not my usual. I more likely hitchhike or walk, anymore. Got too mean on the trains. 'Bout a year ago. Get your throat cut over nothing. I seen it. Just a kid, and he got his throat cut over nothing. Only time I usually ride the train anymore is in one of them autopacs if you can find one full of them big GM cars or some such. Not so easy anymore. Trains around here mostly full of them little Jap trucks."

I asked him if he was a religious man, and he shook his head no.

"I see the Bible on your bedroll, it made me wonder."

"Hell," he said. "I use that entirely for begging, and it ain't the Bible. It's the Book of Mormon. This is Mormon country all through here. They own this state and four others with it. They're all right, though. Better than some. Door to door you quote something out of this book and they'll mostly give you something, especially women, especially older women. Years ago I had some trouble with it, but I hadn't found just the right words was all. Ones I got now is damn near surefire."

When I asked him what they were, he dropped his voice into a pastoral sort of cadence. "You will not suffer that the beggar putteth up his petition to you in vain and turn him out to perish, tho' perhaps thou shalt say the man had brought upon himself his misery, therefore I will stay my hand and not give unto him my food, for his punishments are just, but whosoever doeth this same hath great cause to repent."

"What are you doing in here?"

"Just warming up," he said. "They can't throw me out till after ten, when they hand out the spot work."

The clerk set a stack of applications on the counter, and all of us took one. Just the sight of the thing made me nervous: the bold-print instructions, the long scoreboard of rectangles, each too small for the information it wanted.

I stumbled over the first box, the one that asked my name. If anyone recognized it, my trip was finished. In one way, chances of someone making me seemed slim. It wasn't as if I were Tom Wolfe or Hunter Thompson. But over fifteen years my face and my name had splashed in and out of a lot of magazines, all of which amounted to small beer as fame goes, but now and then it caught up with me in very unlikely places. An oil field in Wyoming would have seemed beyond unlikely except that the magazine I had written for more than any other was bound to be the best-seller in this town. In fact, the kid I'd bought my battery from had closed his copy and slid it quickly out of sight just as I reached his counter. I'd had a quick cold moment when I saw the logo—PLAYBOY—then I told myself to relax. It was the current issue and there was nothing of mine in it, which meant that my mug wasn't in the gallery of authors' photos up front. And even if it had been, the odds that the kid would have scanned the contributors' photos seemed about the same as the odds that he had read whatever article I'd written for that month: about six million to three, the way I figured it.

In the fifteen years I'd been writing for *Playboy*, I'd grown used to the way the hot light of all that pretty young flesh bleached the words around it into near-invisibility. Early on in my career, when I still thought a man ought to be able to make a name, make a living, writing for magazines, I'd worked under the cruel delusion that if I beat my brains out making a fine piece of short nonfiction, the audience would somehow find it. They didn't. Or if they did, they were keeping it to themselves. My very best stories generally drew three or four letters from a circulation of six million. The playmate, no matter what, got a thousand, sometimes two thousand, breathless mash notes a month; and although the lopsidedness of it didn't surprise me, it was a while before I found a simile that took the sting out of the puny response my stories usually got: When people asked, I told them that writing for *Playboy* was something like playing the saxophone in a strip-house band. It was possible that there were one or two people out there in the darkness who noticed your work, but no matter what, you could be pretty damn sure that even they hadn't come for the music.

Finally, though, anonymity that huge has its uses, and you come to trust it. I wrote my name on the application in big block letters, figuring that if by some off-chance someone connected me to *Playboy*, I could just look him in the eye and ask him, if that were me, what the hell I'd be doing worming around Westin when I could be using my pool privileges to play horse-and-rider with the girls in the woo grotto at the big mansion in Beverly Hills?

Where it asked for my education on the application, I gave myself a high school diploma and let it go at that. Somehow, a degree in literature from a Jesuit college didn't seem the kind of ticket that recommended a man for honest work. Besides, it felt good to get the Jesuits out of my history, if only on paper, which is probably the only way anyone ever gets them out.

I spun the story of my working life out of pure smoke. I established construction companies all over the Bay Area, and hired myself on with them in a variety of jobs that finally made it look as if I could have built a house or a bridge with nothing more than a Skilsaw and a set of rough drawings. I gave myself a perfect driving record on everything from a D-9 Caterpillar tractor to a backhoe, and when I remembered that pipe is the cordwood and kindling of the oil fields, I made myself a plumber's apprentice for six months, in San Jose.

While I was writing, I overheard the girl ask about maid work at the Palomino Motel. The clerk told her he didn't like to send people out for that one because the place didn't pay overtime the way it was supposed to, and only gave employees one meal a day instead of two. One of the tattooed men said he was interested in the truck-driving job he'd heard on the radio. The clerk said he'd need a Wyoming driver's license, two years over-the-road experience, and that it was explosives he'd be hauling.

"You can have that shit," said the man.

The two boys were asking about five-dollar-an-hour fry-cook jobs, and the clerk was telling them that nobody he'd sent over there had lasted more than a day in the Mesa Inn kitchens, when I decided to give up filling out the form. The idea of trying to match my pack of lies to the clerk's list of nothing depressed me.

I left the form on the table and said good-bye to the old gypsy with the rotten teeth. He asked me for another cigarette and said I ought to stick around because there was usually some kind of day work that came in. I told him I didn't want day work. "Executive, huh?" he said.

On my way across the street I looked back through the window and saw the guy in the oil-trash T-shirt sit down over my application and begin to copy from it.

The telephone stand in front of the courthouse was busy, but the man who was using it slammed the receiver down just as I got there, and this time when I dialed the fifty-dollar rooms, I got an answer. It turned out to be a rooming house a block from where I was. Yeah, they had a room, said a flat female voice.

I walked past the old brick post office. A hand-lettered sign on the door said there were no post boxes available, don't ask. Across the street at the telephone-company building, half a dozen people waited patiently to use one of the two phones in the foyer that were out of the traffic noise.

Number 400 Main Street was a half-block from the post office; a white clapboard building that had been painted recently enough and quickly enough that the patchy weeds around the foundation were the same color as the walls. Just inside the door a woman in half-glasses sat typing something that looked like contracts. A sign behind her said she was a secretarial service. I told her I wanted to look at the fifty-dollar rooms, and she said the man who took care of that would be back in a minute, and he was—a big man with a big beard, a bucket, and a mop. I told him what I wanted, and he said, "Let me get this out of the way, and I'll show you the only one we've got left." When he got a second look at my face, he said, "What'd you do, go dancing at the Mesa Inn last night?"

He fished through a drawer full of keys, then we went outside and walked the length of the building to a back door.

"Now these is two-man rooms, you understand, but it usually works out good because most of these guys are on different shifts. The room I'm going to show you has a guy working morning tour, so if you got a day job, you'll probably never lay eyes on each other. You working days?"

I told him I was looking.

"It'll work out," he said. "You understand I've got to have two weeks' rent, plus a hundred-dollar damage deposit and ten dollars for the key, right?"

I told him it sounded all right if the place suited me. Just before we went in, he said, "It ain't too whippy in there right now, you understand."

We stepped into a long hallway, and it turned out what he meant by "not too whippy" was that the whole place smelled like fresh vomit.

I said, "Jesus."

"This ain't normal," he said quickly. "There's a real bad son of a bitch on the floor in the bathroom right now. Been there all night. He don't even live here. I just got finished telling him that I was gonna call the cops if he didn't haul his ass outta here in about five minutes. I know the bastard. He used to live here. We got a better class of guys now. Six months ago it was pretty rough."

About halfway down the hall I hesitated.

"I'm gonna have this smell outta here," he said. "In an hour. That's easy. I gotta get that animal drug out first, that's all."

"All right, let's look," I said.

He put the key in the third door of six on the left side of the badly lit hallway. "Like I said, this guy works morning tour, so I don't think he's around." He knocked, and when he heard nothing, he let us in.

"That'd be your bed over there." He was pointing to a bare single mattress on a steel frame up against a plasterboard wall that had been worked over with something that might have been the claw end of a hammer. The only sign that someone slept in the other bed was a filthy, half-shredded sleeping bag that was dripping off the mattress into a large ashtray loaded with the stub ends of unfiltered cigarettes. Next to that were four empty beer cans. The acoustic tile in the ceiling was warped and sprung and missing entirely in a long patch above the window that had a sheet nailed to the frame for a curtain.

" 'Course, if it was much better, it would cost more

than fifty dollars a week," said the man with the beard. "Lot more."

I let him make his excuses, but it wasn't the room that scared me: It was the sleeping bag. It just didn't seem that a man who would lie down in a hopeless rag like that would make much of a roommate. Then again, who the hell did I think I was, and where did I think I was? I'd just spent the night in the animal pens at a rodeo grounds. At least this shitty little room was out of the rain, a foothold, a small piece of territory from which to scout the possibilities. It wasn't exactly a giant step up from the stock pens, but if the landlord really was going to rid the place of the smell, and if the dangerous bastard who slept in that ragged mummy bag did turn out to have different hours from mine, it might work, I thought. Maybe. For a couple of weeks.

"How 'bout it?"

"Well . . . I might. It depends. I think I'll let you clean up the air and check back with you."

"That's no problem. . . ." There was a thump through the wall from the bathroom next door. "Goddamnit to hell," said the landlord. "That's it." Then he stepped into the hall and slammed the bathroom door open. Whoever was inside yelled as if he had been hit in the head.

"Get the fuck outta here," yelled the landlord. "I mean right the fuck now. I've been trying to give you a break, asshole."

The other voice whined something. "Then crawl the fuck outta here," said the landlord. "Because if I have to drag you, it's gonna piss me off worse than I am now, which is about enough to kill you right here."

There was rumbling and banging, then a shirtless man in boots and jeans moved by the room on his hands and knees. The landlord followed as if he were herding something.

"My shirt," said the crawling man.

"Fuck your shirt and get out those steps, you worthless drunk bastard son of a bitch." The two of them disappeared through the door. The landlord came back shaking his head. "I told you it wasn't going to be too whippy in here, but this is not typical, I promise you. I'm just too nice a guy. But I'm going to set off one of those deodorizer bombs in here. That'll take care of it."

"If you can get the smell out, it might work for me," I told him. "But, you know, I can't help wondering what the hell the damage deposit is for." I pointed at the claw marks and the ceiling tile.

"Well," he said in a voice that had all of a sudden lost the salesman's touch, "it's because I don't really know who the hell you are and I don't very much care, and we've had guys take the beds outta here and everything else. The goddamn nails outta the doorjambs." He looked at me to see if I understood. "Besides which, we're gonna do some work around here. Gonna fix this room up in probably a week. And we got a plumber coming in to make the bathroom a little better. You haven't seen that yet, and this ain't the time, because I'll be honest with you, it takes a pretty good beating with ten and twelve people using it. Woulda had it fixed up before now except that if you know anything about Westin, you know it takes about a month to get a plumber out. Anyway, this is it. You see what we got. It's the only thing in town like it. If you want it, and nobody takes it between now and then, we can work it out this afternoon."

On the way back down the hall he told me they were starting a mail service and that I could get a box for thirty bucks a month, two months minimum, ten dollars for the key.

No damage deposit? I almost said, but his sense of humor seemed weak on the point, so I shut up.

Just outside the door the crawling man had heaped up on a patch of hard dirt and was sleeping with his head against the building.

"Get out of my garden, you dirty little wino," said the landlord. "You're going to jail if I find you here on my way back. Jail, you hear me? The hospital." Then he turned to me, pointed to the wino, and said, "We're gonna put some flowers in right here. Gonna look real nice."

The Mesa Inn was the newest, biggest motel in Westin, but that wasn't saying much. Most of the rest were little motor courts left over from the days when this had been a highway stopoff. There were signs in vacant lots all over town that announced plans by this or that hotel chain for something grand, but the Mesa was the first of the big commercial operations to actually get its doors open. They'd hit the boom just right, and they'd done it by using every slapdash and prefab technique they could lay hands on, from the main building, which looked to have had three architects none of whom liked each other, to the boxy dorm outbuildings, to the several acres of treeless blacktop that surrounded it.

The lobby coffee shop had opened the day before I arrived, and it was clear that no one was in charge yet. Every burger, every omelet, that came through the service window sat longer under the heat lamps than it had taken to cook. I watched the man next to me try to cut a piece of liver with a steak knife. The best he could do was deface it. He chased it off his plate twice, and the second time he just left it on the counter, dropped his silverware, and walked quietly out.

The waitresses were taking heavy abuse from the customers, and only one of them seemed to have enough experience to give it back. She was Latin and looked about twenty-five years old, and she had a tattoo on her wrist where a bracelet would have gone. It said she was property of the Road Knights. I tried to ask her for a menu, but as I did, a guy in an aluminum hard hat who'd come from a table near the windows set his coffee in front of her and said, "I can't drink this, honey, and if it wouldn't be out of your way, I'd like a new cup."

"If it's so bad, why'd you drink half of it?" she said.

"Look, lady," he told her. "I waited fifteen minutes for it, that's why. I'm not trying to give you trouble, but look at this stuff." He tipped his cup to show her that it was as much grounds as liquid and that both were the wrong color for coffee. "I can stomach almost anything, but this..."

"The urn ain't working right," she said. "Place has been open forty-eight hours, and everything's broke down."

"I'm not trying to wreck your day," he said.

"I'll give you half a new cup," she said, as if there were something fair about it. He shrugged, and she took his cup to the urn, which sizzled and spit, then poured something that was black at first, then amber.

"This don't look any better," he said.

"Just do what you did with the first cup and drink the top off it," she said, moving back onto the floor without looking at him.

About the time I made my mind up to have a burger and fries if I ever got someone to take my order, one of the waitresses broke into tears in the middle of the floor, not far from the stainless-steel cart that was the salad bar. The other waitresses covied up around her like birds, and I decided that what I needed was a beer, not lunch.

I walked through the lobby past a gift shop, video parlor, liquor store, then down three carpeted stairs into the bar, a tall, wide, windowless room full of western-style tables and chairs. The bar itself ran for twenty or so stools

along one wall and was littered end to end with dirty glass-
ware from what had obviously been a big night. The
woman behind the bar was stocking the beer cooler with
one hand and smoking a cigarette with the other. She had
freshly bleached close-cropped hair, and she was wearing
a white cowboy shirt, a rodeo buckle the size of a tuna can,
and tight black pants that seemed to be saying, "There may
be thirty-five years around the eyes, buster, but look at
this." She was talking to a man who was on top of a fifteen
foot ladder bolting a television camera to the wall.

"I might worry about your little eye in the sky if I
thought it was gonna work," she said. "But since there ain't
one other goddamn thing in this whole joint that works, I
don't see there's anything to fret over."

"It'll work," he told her, "because *I'm* putting it in."

"Yeah? And who put in the cash register, and the glass-
washing machines, and the beer taps and the soda guns?"

"None of them was by me," he said.

I took a stool two down from the only other guy at
the bar, a kid with longish blond hair who was staring into
his beer as if it were about to float a message. He had a
couple of days' stubble on his face and dark circles under
his eyes. I tried to arrange a little space on the bar in front
of me, and in the process forced three tumblers off the
back edge into the well, where they smashed.

"Is it live, or is it Memorex?" said the bartender.

"Sorry," I said. "I didn't mean to..."

"I'll give you five dollars if you'll do that to the rest
of them," she said. "What you want?"

"Budweiser."

"How 'bout a nice warm Schlitz," she said, holding up
a can from the box she was loading. "I'd offer you a glass,
but you've had yours." A minute later she answered the
phone, then talked to the man on the ladder. "They're
ready to focus, they say."

"Hold on, tell 'em."

From what I'd overheard about the Mesa Inn, I'd assumed the camera was being installed to monitor the crowd along the bar, but when the man on the ladder had finished turning the swivel bolt, the lens was pointed exactly at the cash register.

"What?" said the bartender into the phone. "I don't know why I should...all right...all right." She stretched the phone cord till she was standing in front of the register, then she looked up into the camera. "This it?...Smile, my ass," she said, and then gave the boys in the back room perhaps the most demure finger I have ever seen. "Focus on that," she told them.

"She's got the right attitude, anyway," said the kid on the stool next to me.

"Pretty much," I said. He smiled over at me as if he were ill. He was wearing a black T-shirt and a leather jacket, and hanging from his neck was a short gold chain with a Harley Davidson eagle and a Saint Christopher on it. I asked him if he was working.

"Was," he said. "Now, I don't know. Probably not. I think I'm run off. I know I am. I been missing in action for two days...I think it's two days...what's today... Tuesday. Then I'm run off for sure. I woke up in Salt Lake this morning, and I don't even remember going there. I'm going to see my boss as soon as I straighten out a little. He's going to run me off, though."

When I asked him what he was doing, he said, "Riding the choppers, seismic exploration, you know, planting explosives out in the forest."

"I think I heard helicopters going out this morning," I told him. "They just lost one of those, didn't they?"

"That was my outfit," he said. "Wasn't my crew, but I saw it. We come in about two minutes after it happened.

Jesus. Looked down, saw this fucking chopper laying out there like a shot duck." He took the last half of his beer in two swallows. "I hate flying anyway, so I definitely did not want to see that. They gave us the rest of the day off, which is when I got fucked up. I think I went over to Big Mormon with a woman. I'm not sure."

When I offered, he said yeah, he'd have one more beer before he went to see if he still had a job. We talked for about an hour—four beers. His name was Steve Bohannon, and he'd come from Florida to Rock Springs two years before. He'd worked half a dozen oil-field jobs before he found the seismic work. Good money, he said, although he kept spending most of it on motorcycles, which were what he really loved. He said he'd just bought a Harley Sturgis with belt drive that was in Salt Lake getting five hundred dollars worth of chrome put on it. He was living in the Mesa with three roommates, paying for it with the fifty dollars a day subsistence money that went with his salary. Wasn't bad work if you didn't count the flying, he said. Better than worming around the rigs. You got a better class of guy on the seismic crews.

About the time he told me that, a huge man in an old pair of denim overalls shuffled up behind us and said, "You got any money?"

Steve turned around and said, "Animal . . . I been looking for you. I think I'm run off—no, I don't have any money. Am I run off?"

When I turned, I was looking at a huge man with a crew cut and sad eyes who would have had a lovable Brer Bear sort of presence about him except for the swastika tattooed exactly in the middle of his forehead.

Steve asked him if he'd talked to their boss, and Animal said yes, but just long enough to get his final check. Then Steve asked him if he was quitting because of the crash, and Animal said no. He'd had a bad go-round with the college-boy prick field supervisor that ended with him getting run off, which was all right with him because he was quitting anyway.

"What about me? Am I run off?" Steve asked him.

"Doubt it," said Bear. "The skinny kid from Oklahoma quit this morning, so they gonna be shorthanded."

Animal said he was on his way to Texas and asked Steve if he wanted to buy his final check, which was gonna take three days to come through and he didn't want to wait around. It was going to be for six hundred dollars, and he offered to sell it for four hundred cash. Steve said all his cash had gone for chrome in Salt Lake.

The two of them walked out together, but Steve left a fresh beer on the bar and said he'd be back as soon as he talked to his boss, who had an office in the hotel. Five minutes later he came smiling down the stairs.

"I'm not run off," he said. "Close call, though. Animal was right. They're shorthanded, which is all that saved my ass."

"Think I might get hired?" I said.

"There's a chance."

"Do I need experience?"

"Not when they're short," he said. Then he told me the best thing to do was to show up for muster at 7:00 A.M. the next morning, which was when they hired. He gave me the number of the room Ibex Seismic was using as headquarters.

An hour later I was back in the office of the Main Street rooming house. The manager was finishing up on the phone with a plumber.

"... Thing's getting to the point where it barely flushes and it's just not going to hold up another week is what I'm thinking...."

What I heard of the conversation would have bothered me more, except that the beers and the prospect of a job had taken the panic out of the day and given me the false sense that I could stand anything for a month. In fact, I'd had enough beer that there was a dangerous sort of romance creeping back into the whole project.

"Smells a whole lot better in there now," said the landlord when he hung up. "But you can tell me."

It was starting to rain again as we walked the length of the building, past the spot where the drunk had been curled. The back door was open, and even before I got to the top step, the chemical smell that tries to resemble a pine forest hit me.

"This stuff will fade out," said the landlord. "Needs a little time, that's all."

I asked to see the bathroom.

"Sure," he said. "Now you remember I told you it was a bit run-down. Got a plumber coming in tomorrow, early, I think."

It could be worse, was my first thought. There was a big claw-foot bathtub along one wall. The linoleum tile was scaling up around the edges, and the sink was missing one of its long chrome legs and leaning hard, and the commode was leaning too, but just slightly. Otherwise it was decent. The hot water was hot, the mirror was in one piece, there was no writing on the walls, and standing there in the piney air looking at the stormy evening sky through the open window, I decided I could do worse.

"I'll take it," I said.

I signed the papers, handed over $210, and took a key. I didn't leave my gear, though. I still had a picture of Animal in my head, and before I moved all the way in, I wanted to meet my roommate. Read his tattoos.

3

I spent the rest of the afternoon driving the outskirts of town past makeshift industrial yards with their big tin garages and trailer-home offices. Several of them had signs out that said NOT HIRING, but they didn't bother me. I was trying to imagine myself riding helicopters and digging holes for dynamite, wondering what you did when the sky turned to soup and the rain started blowing sideways the way it was this evening. I wondered if they carried tents, or if you just had to huddle in the grounded choppers till the storm passed.

I decided to call Suzanne before I had a chance to hang any more doubts into my mood. Before I'd pissed away my beery optimism.

Both the phones in the foyer of the Mountain Bell offices were empty when I got to them, but as I dialed, a drunken old man in a straw Stetson used the weight of his body to open the door. He dumped a noisy pocketful of change on the little metal shelf.

Suzanne answered the phone, and for that first mo-

ment the sound of her voice washed me with a cold, sep-
arate feeling. She said she missed me. I told her the same.

"Hello, dollface," said the drunk, then he listened for
a minute. "No, no, no. I ain't down at the Silver Horn, I'm
over in Westin still... I'm working... yes I am... no I'm
not... don't *be* that way... I ain't drunk and I'll swear that
to you... I'm tired as a dog, that's all."

I told Suzanne that I had a place to stay and that I
might have a job in the morning. That's great, that's fast,
she said, but the way she said it told me she'd heard something in my voice that was a little shaky about both pros-
pects. I told her the room was pinned down, but the job
was still a maybe. On a rig? she wanted to know. Helicopters, I told her. Seismic work. I didn't say anything about
the explosives.

"It's raining like the Bible around here, baby," said
the old cowboy. "I can't see how I'm gonna drive back into
Salt Lake tonight. It's foolish out there, honey.... No,
goddamnit now, I told you I ain't been drinking. They just
now finished unloading the truck, and I came right over
here to call you. You understand? I was thinking about
you, honey. I figured you might worry when I didn't..."

Suzanne told me she'd been busy—company picnic to
plan, three people to hire, four salary reviews that week—
but that she was happy for the work because it kept her
from thinking too much about me. She asked nothing
about the room or the job, and while she talked about some
trouble she was having with her car, I found myself con-
centrating on the things I didn't want to tell her, which
was making for small, stumbling starts when it came my
turn to talk.

"Now damnit, I didn't phone you up so you could tell
me I was a alcoholic... and I... all right. I'll tell you what.
I'll just go ahead and get out on the highway in this rain
and put me and the truck in a ditch. That make you happy?

Then don't you think I might oughta just sleep right here in the truck tonight?...Goddamnit no...now that makes me mad. They ain't any women in this town anyway. You know that. And there ain't no whores, neither...."

Suzanne asked me if I was all right, and when I told her everything was fine so far, she asked if I was sure. I told her I was tired. Then I said that Westin was pretty raw from what I'd seen so far, but that I'd expected it to be raw and that my spirits were holding. I said I was going to get a little Chinese food for dinner, then go over to the Mesa for a drink, then back to my room to move in. She said she was going out for a drink, too, after work with a couple of girlfriends, Joan and Tracy. Both of them were a mess, she said. Tracy's husband had caught her in an affair, and Joan was thinking about confessing hers to her husband. Crazy stuff, she said. Time to commiserate.

"Well, now I *am* going to get drunk," said the old man. "The hell with it. No, I ain't coming home tonight. I'll come home when I feel like it and when I'm finished working and when it stops raining...and when I'm sober, that's right...Well, if he's that sick, you go ahead and shoot him, I don't care. He's a woman's dog anyway, always has been...."

"How's the greenhouse?" I asked.

"I was just going out to check it right now," Suzanne said.

I hung up sorry that I'd called, sorry about what I'd given away in the pauses and inflections, hating the guesses that her pauses and inflections had set loose in my head.

"Takes care of that," said the old drunk, scraping his change up. "It's like going to church."

I had chow mein at a Station Street joint called Low's. The rain stopped while I was eating, and I decided to leave the Maverick where it was and walk to the Mesa. It was only about a mile and a half, and the route would take me

along the street with the big elms and old houses that was
the only pretty moment in the whole town. I thought it
might work a little bit on my sinking mood. The elms were
still dripping, and the lawns were heaving up the green
smell they get late on a warm wet day.

The thing that was eating me most about the phone
call was the greenhouse business. I'd been gone two days,
and it didn't sound as if Suzanne had been out there even
once. If it got hot, it was only going to take one day to
burn the crop to the same yellow as the summer hills, and
there would be no bringing it back from that color. I tried
to tell myself to write it off; that the plants were probably
going to be lost among the gossip and intrigues and com-
miserating that Suzanne had been so preoccupied with
even before I left. I got a picture of the proud, callow
stalks and limbs dropping onto each other, dying.

Which was why the Lord invented whiskey, I told myself.

The bar at the Mesa Inn was braced for the evening
by the time I got there. A sign at the door set the dress
code: no torn T-shirts, no work clothes, no greasy boots.
The bouncer looked as if he might be working the job so
that he could buy more weights, enough maybe to make
the distinction between his neck and his head disappear
completely. He was wearing a white polo shirt that fit as
if it weren't going to survive a deep breath. He took a two-
dollar cover charge from me without saying anything.
Then he stamped the back of my hand with a big inky
word, IN. There's my tattoo, I thought.

About half the saloon-style tables were four and five
around with big young men in clean hats and shirts for
the evening. Most of them had beer in a bottle or a can,
and some of them had a shot glass next to that.

There was one seat at the bar next to the waitress

station, and I climbed in. Looking up and down the bar at the thirty or so other men, I couldn't help feeling hatless. There were two waitresses working the floor. One of them was a child-sized woman whose eyes and nose and mouth were magazine perfect. Some of the men stared at her openly, constantly, and all of them flirted heavily when she delivered their drinks, bending in her tight jeans, her tight camisole top; and though she smiled here and there, it was in flashes only. Then her face would square back to the photo-cool that I imagined had ridden in a hundred wallets wherever she'd gone to high school.

She stood between the chrome rails of the waitress station, ordered six Lite beers and six shots of tequila, looked at me without looking, then sidestepped to make room for the other waitress, who was large, probably forty-five years old, and the perfect, homely contrast to the little princess.

I overheard the man three stools down saying, "... 'course, I'm only there one month in four or five, but it's probably just as good that way. I bought her a Thunderbird a while back, and she's got her forty-dollar nail jobs and every other damn thing she wants, so she don't complain too much. Anyways, she's number three, and she knows damn well that if she starts bitching, I'll just take up with Mrs. Four."

"But what the hell you do when you're up here?" said the man next to him. "I'm 'bout going crazy. I'm to the point it hurts."

"The fat girls is always available," said the man next to him.

The woman who'd been stocking the bar that afternoon was still behind it, and she didn't look pleased with her double shift. She asked me, "What's yours," and I ordered a double scotch with a lemon twist and almost immediately thought better of it. Shots and beers stood

Mutt and Jeff all up and down the bar, and I was going to be sitting there with an effete little lemon rind floating around in my big-city cocktail. Mercifully, the bartender delivered it without the lemon, and I didn't ask her for it. She took five dollars from me, and three dollars from the man next to me, rang four dollars into the computer cash register, and stuffed the rest into the beer schooner she was using for a tip jar. I looked up for the little red light on the TV camera and it was on, but the speed and confidence of the rodeo lady's move made it seem entirely unlikely that electronics were going to catch her skimming.

About the time the crowd got two deep behind me, I spotted Steve. He and a pretty girl were sliding onto a couple of seats at the right-angle end of the bar. She had almost-blond hair pulled into a long braid with a feather hanging in it. Steve recognized me about the time their drinks arrived and held up his beer by its long neck as if to say hi.

"You know that guy?" said a voice next to me. There was a sharp southern accent to it, and when I turned, I was looking at a round, boyish face under a corp cap that said MUD on it.

"He and I met this afternoon," I told him.

"Tell you what," he said. "I wish sometimes I was a long haired son-of-a-bitch motorcycle bum when I see 'em with the pretty little ones like that."

I didn't say anything. He seemed about half-drunk, and I didn't want to get into it with him.

"Them women love motorcycles, though, don't they? Like horses." He pointed at the bartender's belt buckle. "Ain't that right, Sal? Bet you love horses, don't you?"

Sal looked at him as she lifted six beers out of the cooler in front of us. "I don't settle bar bets, and I don't answer questions 'bout love," she said, and moved away.

"She's a pistol, ain't she?" said MUD. "Tell you what.

If I owned a woman like that, I'd know how to work her."

Steve and his girl finished their beers, and on the way to the door he stopped to say he'd see me in the morning at five-thirty, room 206. I told him I'd be there.

"You work with him, do ya?" said MUD.

"Find out tomorrow," I said. "His crew's short-handed."

"So you *looking* for work then?"

"Yup. Like everybody else in this town, I guess."

"Ever work derrick hand?"

"No," I said. "This is my first oil field."

"You ain't never been in the patch before? And you come here? Shee-it." He pulled back a bit to get a better look at me. "Tell you what. You could not have picked a worse field to break in. This is the wormiest operation I ever saw, and I seen 'em all over the world since I was thirteen years old and I'm thirty-five next month."

Sal asked us if we wanted another drink, and when I said yes, MUD said he'd have another Budweiser and to take mine out of the twenty-dollar bill on the bar in front of him. Then he lit a cigarette, looked at me again, and shook his head.

"How old are ya?" he said. I told him thirty-three. "What the hell are you doing trying to come into the patch at thirty-three years old?"

I told him I needed the money.

"Well, you might make some money here, all right, if these wormy sombitches don't kill you first." He looked at his beer. Dusted an ash off his white jeans. " 'Course, if somebody broke you in good, you might be all right. I could do that . . . if I wanted . . . if you was worth a shit. I'm a pusher over at D and J." When I asked him what a pusher was, he said, "Boy, you really don't know nothing what-soever, do ya?"

I already told you I didn't know anything, you nasty

bastard, I was going to say, but I didn't.

"Normal thing is for a rig to carry five men," he said. "Worm, motor hand, chain hand, derrick hand, and the driver. That's a full crew. Tool pusher's the guy that hires 'em all, then makes sure they stay sober and have everything they need in the way of equipment to keep the rig running. Also sees they don't get lazy or stupid, which they mostly are anyways. Should be one pusher for one rig, but D and J is just starting up, so I got three rigs I'm pushing for. Got two brand-new ones we building over in the yard right now. Biggest rigs in Wyoming, Cooper 750s."

The band was setting up in a far corner of the room under a wall mural that had buffalo running alongside a steam engine. Two guitarists squeezed themselves onto the little bandstand in front of the drum set, and one of them tested the microphone. He asked twice to have it turned louder, and when nothing happened, he turned to his partners, shrugged, and they began with a tune of their own called "Jesus Said to Love Your Neighbor, but You Don't Have to Bring Them All Home."

"Where'd you come here from?" said MUD.

"San Francisco."

"Frisco?" he said. "Nothing out there but queers and spears, what I heard."

"Tell you what," I said, using his accent. "Why don't you just drink your beer and pick this evening's fight with somebody else." There was a pause while I looked him straight in the face and thought, Oh shit, here we go.

"Now don't get all pissed on," he said. "I didn't mean nothing by that. I ain't never even been to Frisco. I was just talking. You got a temper, though, don't ya?"

"It's been a bad day," I told him. "And yesterday wasn't too whippy, either."

"This is a bad place if you ain't got a job. 'Course, I

could line that out for ya right here, if I wanted."

He looked at his beer as if it were my turn to say
something. I didn't.

"How much school you got?" he said.

"Too much, probably."

"You got college?"

I nodded.

"How many years?"

"All four," I told him.

"Shit," he said. "And you out of work. Don't make
sense. I barely got through ninth grade, and I never been
outta work except when I wanted to be. My daddy put me
in the patch when I was twelve years old, me and my
brothers. He used to say, 'I could send you to college for
ten years, and you'd just come out queer.'"

I had my second big scotch all the way in me when he
said that, and I was beginning to see the humor of the
whole exchange. There was something about MUD that
didn't mean to be hostile, no matter what he said. He was
trying to be cocky, but it wasn't quite working. He just
wanted to talk to somebody, and anybody would have done
that night. It occurred to me that his daddy had probably
also told him that anybody who drank alone was an alcoholic.

"College boy," he said. "I'll be damned. This place is
so full of trash you just don't expect it."

"Strange times," I said.

"What did you take when you was at college?"

"Literature."

"You was probably a English teacher, wasn't you, I'll
bet."

I smiled and didn't say anything.

"I figured," he said. "That's the only thing you can
do with literature for your background. And you got laid
off, huh?"

I nodded. We watched the bartender bend over, then move away.

"You a drunk?"

"Not yet," I told him.

"I see you drinking that hard stuff is why I asked. I never touched a drop of that stuff since I was in the navy. I woke up in a shore-patrol launch in handcuffs. That was gin. Beat some SP about half to death, they told me. Did thirty days in the brig. Just said to myself, Gin's gonna kill ya. Was you in service?"

"No."

"You didn't miss nothing," he said. "You queer?"

I laughed. "Not yet," I said, "but looking around this room, I might have to consider it if I get a job that keeps me in this town for very long."

"I'm thinking about bringing my wife up from Texas for a few days myself."

The pretty little bar waitress pulled into the station next to me and ran off a list of drinks that sounded like a takeout order for the James gang. Then she asked the bartender to tell the bouncer that there was a woman at a table in the far corner with a gun in her purse.

"I could hire ya right here and now," said MUD, squinting sideways at me.

"What kind of work?" I said.

"Put you in the yard, break you in right, then get you out worming on one of the rigs. I got a couple of worms I'm gonna be running off in the morning . . . so I got room for ya. I'm just afraid you'll get one paycheck and take off, that's all. Depends if you're worth a shit."

"I have to check on that helicopter job in the morning. . . ."

"The hell with that," he said. "You just show up tomorrow morning at eight o'clock in the yard, and I'll put you on. You hired."

"How much does it pay?"

"Eight dollars and twenty-five cents an hour," he said. "I know that don't sound like much, but that's for the first forty hours a week. I'll get you sixty or seventy hours and it's time and a half after forty, so's you'll do all right. Plus there's other sidelights in the patch. You'll make some money, don't worry. If you's worth a shit."

I asked him where the yard was. "You just walk out this door and look west," he said, pointing toward the bandstand. "The tallest derrick you see, right next to the highway, is the one we're rigging right now. Biggest rig in Wyoming...Cooper 750."

He slurred the word *biggest*.

"I'll be there," I said. "What's your name?"

"Sonny," he said, shaking my hand. "You be there." Then he looked at me sideways. "College boy," he said. "Ain't that a thing."

On the walk back across town in the damp air, I thought of calling Suzanne to tell her I had a job, but it was late, my balance wasn't good. Sonny had bought us several rounds after he hired me, and they'd pretty much put a hat on the evening's drunk for both of us. When I left, he was slow-babbling, sometimes to me, sometimes to his beer, sometimes to the man on his left: about one of his brothers, Bub. Something about a woman between them, somebody's wife, I thought I heard him say.

I rooted through the trunk of the Maverick in the pale yellow shine of a street lamp. I got my sleeping bag, flashlight, a notebook, and the knife, walked around the back of my rooming house and let myself in. The pine bomb had worn off enough to let some of the natural stink of the place into the mix, but it wasn't that bad. Whatever lights hung in the hall were out, so I found my door by flashlight, then stood there for a minute listening to a terrible wet snoring. It didn't sound like it was coming from my room, which was good, because the power and resonance of it suggested someone twice my size who wasn't taking care of himself.

I opened the door slowly and shone the light on both beds. Empty. And all of a sudden I felt just fine. The relief of not having to face my roommate just then let my drunk sweep over me, and there was a strange, weary happiness to the moment. I laid my sleeping bag on the bare bed, set my wristwatch for 6:00 A.M., lay back, and was gone.

The next thing I heard sounded like someone trying to fish something out of a deep jar with a knife. I grabbed the flashlight. A key ring hit the floor in the hall, a drunken voice said "goddamnit," then the scraping, a key trying to find a keyhole, took up again. I got my feet out of my bag and on the floor, grabbed my flashlight, and tried to remember where the hell I'd stashed the knife.

The door opened, and I put the beam of my light into the eyes of a smaller man than I'd expected. He jerked back, covered his face with his forearm, and said, "Don't shoot." He had a beer in one hand and another ten or fifteen in his voice.

"I'm not going to shoot," I said, which was meant to freeze him where he stood by holding out the possibility that I actually did have a gun pointed at him. He had a delicate face and skinny arms. His T-shirt and jeans were filthy black, and he smelled like oil.

"Who the fuck are you?" he said.

"I think we're roommates," I told him.

"Well, then, for shitsakes what are you pointing that gun at me for?" he said.

"I don't have a gun," I said.

"Oh Christ, that's good," he said, lurching into the room toward his bed. "Twice in one night would have been too much . . . too much." He set his beer on the floor, kicked

it over taking his pants off, then he lay down. I waited for
him to talk or snore, but there was neither. Just heavy
breathing that grew slower, deeper.

I lay on one elbow, felt my adrenaline drain away, my
eyes close. Then I heard the crying. I thought it was a
dream at first, then I felt something in my chest and I
thought it was me, but it wasn't. It was my roommate. It
began in soft, broken sobs, then became a small, steady
weeping. I lifted my head and asked if he was all right,
but he was out. Twice the crying became a snore, and twice
it broke back into childlike tears, then turned to sighs, and
finally to soft, peaceful breathing.

The notebook I began the next morning opened with
the words *You are never doing what you think you're doing*,
and when I read them now, they have the unmistakable
stink of the little Zen sermons I usually give myself when
I begin to realize how much trouble I'm really in. I was
making the notes at the wheel of the Maverick. The sun
was just up, and I was parked across the street from the
D and J yard, which was deserted except for a white dog
who was smelling his way around the base of the chain-
link fence that was the perimeter. The word *run* does not
appear on the first page, but I remember thinking it. In
fact, I remember thinking that my situation was beginning
to look entirely too much like poor stupid Mr. Bizonni's
in those moments when he crept up on what he thought
was that sleeping garbage-dump grizzly in Yellowstone: a
mauling for sure. The only question was how bad.

It wouldn't have done to write it that way that morning, though. Better to make a quick, crude map of the
territory and salt it with just enough landmark and detail
so that later, years later maybe, I could look back and
decide just what in hell I really had been doing.

I turned the book sideways and drew the three-acre

dirt rectangle that the fence enclosed. The southern edge of the property sat in the shoulder culvert of old 80, which I labeled *Hwy* in a shaky scrawl that reminds me when I read it now of the nasty hangover I was working with. I don't know how long I'd slept that night. I remember being awakened before dawn by something that sounded like a game of catch with a bag of rocks. It turned out to be my roommate grinding his teeth, and though it didn't seem to be wrecking his sleep at all, it was the end of mine, so I got my things together, got in the Maverick, and drove through first light to the Broken Wheel for a Styrofoam cup of coffee, then across town to D and J, which I found, as Sonny had said I would, by guiding on the huge derrick. It stood along the highway edge of the yard, and when I drew it into my map, I estimated that it was a hundred feet tall. It soared up off the rear of a huge truck like the extended ladder of a fire engine. Just in front of it were side-by-side diesel engines about the size of Volkswagen buses, and in front of them, the driver's cab.

An old pickup with a camper shell stood along the fence at the western edge of the yard. Racks of heavy pipe sat nearby, along with spools of cable as big as wagon wheels. A long aluminum garage filled the northeast corner of the lot, and behind that another rig, this one with its derrick telescoped down to fifty feet and laid lengthwise over the truck as if it were ready to go looking for oil. There was a small crane truck parked near the garage, a couple of portable toilets against the southern fence, a scatter of fifty-gallon drums near the middle of things, heaps of scrap metal here and there.

Except for the dog, nothing was moving. The sky was perfectly clear. Small birds worked the warm, dry breeze up and down between the top of the fence and the clumpy patches of prairie grass. I drank my coffee, wrote in my notebook.

* * *

. . . the dog has spotted me. Big white Lab, looks like. Just staring at me, just curious. Stocky man in a red bandanna, two buckets, comes out of the garage. Dog delighted, jumping, barking. "Oil, you worthless hound, get outta here, get down, go eat a groundhog," he says . . . A white dog named Oil . . . That figures: the boys' school nickname cruelty that calls the fat boy slim, the bald man curly . . . sitting here with the same edgy feeling I've had how many times? Every schoolyard, gym class, playing field, summer camp, shop class . . . waiting to line up with strange boys, to feel for your place in the pack . . . getting ready to suffer whatever bullshit little initiations they trade around in this sandlot . . . trying to spot the guys who hate you on sight, the guys who know the ropes, the soreheads, the quiet ones, the gung ho, the slackers, the drunks and the stoners, the skinny ones who can lift twice their weight, the ones who limp but aren't hurt, the ones who are hurt but don't limp, the jokers, the thieves, the storytellers.

Around seven-thirty, a white pickup with a D and J sticker on the doors pulled into the dirt drive. One of the five men in the crew cab got out and opened the gate. As the truck rolled through, he hopped onto the big steel bumper under the tailgate. When the driver saw him there, he punched it, a geyser of dust enveloped the rear of the truck, which took off in a series of skidding figure eights that finally spit the clinging man ten feet out of the dirty cloud and rolled him another ten across the hard ground. He got up holding his elbow; then, while he walked to retrieve his hard hat, the fat man who'd stepped from the driver's seat yelled, "You gotta ride to the buzzer or you don't get no points, cowboy." Then he laughed as if it were the little moments like this that made getting up in the morning worth the trouble.

Over the next ten minutes two bobtail welding trucks drove onto the yard, an old Plymouth dropped three hands at the gate, and a kid on a motorcycle cruised in wearing a hockey helmet. He was followed by a catering truck, which blew a couple of bars of "Dixie" on its horn, then parked in the long morning shadow of the derrick. The driver got out, threw open the quilted chrome panels on the sides, and shouted, "Java, it's java."

I drove the Maverick onto the yard and parked it along the fence. As I got out and started toward the catering truck, another D and J truck came onto the yard as if it were being chased. I just got out of its way and saw Sonny behind the wheel as it went by. He didn't look happy. He skidded the truck up next to the gathered hands and yelled out the window at the fat man.

"You got nothing to do around here, is that it? Nobody works unless I'm here. I swear to God I'll run you and your whole damn crew off if you don't find things to do around here."

The fat man was looking straight at Sonny, and what he wasn't saying was all over his face: Don't push too far . . . you're not big enough for the job. His crew was looking away and at the ground, as were the rest of the hands.

"I want you rigging the brake today," Sonny told the fat man. "And I want your crew to wash the rig real good all the way up."

The fat man nodded slowly, then sent two of his hands for buckets, brushes, soap, and rags. When Sonny spotted me, he drove ten feet to where I was standing and said, "Well, College, you made it. That's good. I want to talk to you later. You go ahead and start swabbing the rig with Tom's crew. And be smart up there. Watch where you put your feet. I got to run that other worm off."

I watched him drive another ten feet to a young hand who listened for a minute, then did a little pleading. Finally, Sonny told him, "You was missing two days, and you wasn't worth that much while you was here. Just stop over to the office, get a check, and go on down the road." He left the kid standing there and drove off the yard.

I walked over to the group with the buckets. The fat man was saying something angry about Sonny, which he interrupted in midsentence when he saw me. "What are you looking for?" he said.

"Sonny told me to work with your crew today."

"My ass," he said. "I don't need no more crew. You just tell Sonny to find you something else." He turned to walk away.

"You tell him," I said. He stopped the way a batter stops when he's a few steps toward first base on ball four, then hears the umpire call strike three...a skinny little umpire. He looked at me as if I were the second person he'd wanted to kill that morning but couldn't; as if I'd be a lot easier to kill than Sonny if it came down to that.

"All right," he said. "You want to wash, you can wash. You can start in the crown." He pointed to the top of the rig. "You get you a bucket and a brush and you climb till you're looking at the sheaves. Then you start washing."

"What are the sheaves?" I asked him.

"Shit," he said. "You ain't too wormy, are you? You ever been on any kind of rig at all? No, you haven't, have you? Well then, this ought to be real fun for you, if you don't fall down and get yourself dead." He smiled and put his hand on my shoulder. "Now you're going to be real careful up there, aren't you? Specially when the wind comes up the way it does. You go ahead and get on that thing over there with the rungs in it—that's called a ladder—and you keep climbing till you run out of rig, and you'll be looking right at the sheaves." Then, without taking his eyes off me, he said, "Get him a bucket, Marlin, and get one for yourself."

Marlin was a big kid with a quiet face, the one who'd been thrown from the bumper of the truck. "Marlin don't

much like heights," said the fat man, "but we're going to
cure him. He's going to follow you up, then the two of you
work your way down."

Marlin seemed as if he might say something, then
didn't, then looked at me as if the whole thing were my
fault, as if I'd somehow drawn the meanness out of the fat
man and he'd been splashed by accident.

I took one of the large plastic buckets from him,
dropped a stiff brush into the soapy water, and carried it
to the base of the rig. The bucket was a little over half-
full and weighed about fifteen pounds. The fat man and
his crew watched me as I set it down and relaced my
boots. All right, you fat bastard, I thought, watch this: I
don't know a sheave from a drill bit and I've maybe held
a pipe wrench twice in my life, but today's the day I get
on this derrick and make you look the fool you are, because if there's one thing I can do, it's climb, and I mean
buildings or trees or the rocks that make Yosemite beautiful and famous... and if you think the perfect iron ge-
ometry of this stubby little oil rig holds even small fright
for a guy who's clung from a dirty little one-finger crack
fifteen times as high as your goddamn sheaves, then just
watch this.

I swung into it and got about ten rungs up before I
had to stop and make some adjustments. The heavy bucket
was putting a serious limp into my moves. My rubber-soled
boots didn't feel very good on the round steel rungs, either.

"You only got a hundred feet to go," said the fat man.
"Don't get tired, now."

That pretty much did it. I let the bucket slide into the
crook of my right arm so that I could get both hands on
the ladder, and I started climbing as if macho were oxygen,
as if anger were muscle, which they are for a while, but
never for long on the vertical. Thirty feet up I felt myself
moving into the zone where the bill comes due on what

you've spent, where gravity seems to double, where everything that was slightly awkward becomes a torture. My grip was going soft, the arm with the bucket on it was trying to cramp, and my mind was beginning to whine into the ear of the animal that we had to rest . . . that there was no safety line and why wasn't there any safety line? . . . that we could have climbed first, then hauled the bucket up on a rope . . . that the whole thing was dangerously foolish, and that if I went on taking playground-style dares from every nasty kid in the yard, there was a good chance I was going to be hurt. Badly. I stopped. I balanced the bucket on the rung above my feet, then hung to the full length of my arm so that my bones took the weight instead of my muscles. I breathed. I looked down . . . about sixty feet, I thought . . . and there were the fat man and his crew craning their heads back, shading their eyes.

There was a platform twenty feet above me, a steel grating that ran all the way around the derrick: plenty of room to stand and set the bucket down, get a real rest. I took another minute's breath, got the bucket over my left arm, and this time I put my mind with my feet and began moving one rung at a time. That was the solution, of course; a simple old formula that I can never seem to remember short of whipping and threatening and humiliating myself. Maybe that ought to be your tattoo, I told myself as I swung up onto the platform: PAY ATTENTION. Maybe write the words across a giant eyeball on the back of your hand.

I set the bucket down and shook my arms out. The little iron balcony looked like a workstation, probably for the derrick hand, I thought. I wasn't sure what he did, but he had a great view of Westin from up there: the hills, the sawmill, the river, and the railroad tracks that cut through town along its banks. The sun was warm, the breeze light, and for the first time I noticed a beautiful old roundhouse on the western edge of town. It looked to be a hundred years old, and the railroad was still using it. There were bays for a dozen engines arranged in a circle around the short stretch of track that rotated them in and out of the freight yards. While I watched an engine turn, I heard a lovely throaty whistle, and the cross-country Amtrak passenger liner from Oakland came out of the hills and slid through the valley, then disappeared through a rocky notch on the east.

I heard the fat man shouting, and when I looked down, I saw Marlin standing at the base of the rig with his bucket. Christ, I thought. Hauling a pail of water and a fear of heights up this ladder was going to be an awful piece of work. He stood on the bottom rung anyway, which made me guess that he was more afraid of the fat man than he was of altitude; then he stepped back down, and I wondered. The fat man yelled again, and this time Marlin got onto the ladder again and started slowly up. He must need this job worse than I've ever needed one, I thought. The morning was less than an hour old, he had already been thrown from the back of a truck, and now he was making his way up toward what would surely be panic when he passed the point at which the body knows by instinct that a fall could mean death. About ten feet up he stopped and hugged the ladder. He didn't look up, and he didn't look down. He stayed where he was, breathing badly, till the fat man shouted again; then he began moving, pausing on every rung as if it might be his limit. He stopped again just over thirty feet up, and this time he almost lost the bucket when he tried to get a full-body grip on the ladder. He managed to hang on, but from where I was, I heard him whimper in a way I'd heard before, in a way I'd whimpered myself just before I took a sixty-foot screamer off a rock called Royal Arches. It's a pathetic sound that comes up from a place inside that has accepted the inevitability of what's about to happen. The difference was that on Royal Arches I'd been on a rope that had saved me.

Marlin was clamped to the ladder like a mollusk, which was good because panic was all over him. If he tried to move, he was going to fall.

"Pour the water out," I shouted.

"I can't," he said without looking up.

"Drop the bucket."

When he didn't answer, I started down. I stopped two rungs above him. "Don't move. Try to relax," I said, even though I knew that nothing sounds more ridiculous when you are where he was. "Focus on your breathing," I said. Then I sat into the rung I was on, locked my feet around the sides of the ladder, then leaned out backward and down.

"Let me have the bucket," I said. Nothing. "All right, hold on with your left arm and just let go with your right long enough for me to get the bucket off." Still nothing. I reached down and got the handle of the bucket, lifted the weight of it off his arm. "Now just let loose long enough for me to get it out of here." He looked up at me. All the fear in the world was on his face. "We're all right," I said. "Just let me take the bucket." He let go, I lifted it free, and he dived back into his cling.

I looked down and saw the fat man and his crew watching us. Just for a second I thought of dropping the whole goddamn bucket on them. Instead, I poured it out and watched them scatter as the soapy foam broke into a shower and sprayed them.

"Got 'em," I said.

"Oh man, don't fuck with Tom," Marlin said without looking down. "He came back from Nam real violent."

Great, I thought. One of the unexploded walking bombs from the war. Probably ambushed in the jungle and has never been able to talk about it. Probably all right as long as the death anger doesn't build up, as long as he can throw somebody from a moving truck once a day.

"Do you want to climb down?"

"I can't go down," he said.

"Then let's go up to the platform. Take it slow, rest as often as you want, one step at a time, nothing to it. Here we go."

I did five rungs, then saw Marlin begin to climb slowly, putting a careful pause between each move. About a minute after I reached the platform, he pulled himself up next to me and sat on the grating, breathing hard. Neither of us said anything.

I saw the fat man walking off toward the tin shed with one of his crew. The other two were climbing with their buckets onto the wide lower beams of the rig. The only man on the ground still watching us was the guy wearing the red bandanna.

"Who's that?" I said.

"Reno," said Marlin. "The yard boss."

"Just the man I want to talk to," I said. I grabbed the empty bucket, got on the ladder, and climbed down. The white dog met me and smelled me, then jumped alongside as I walked over to where Reno was standing.

"Wonder if there's a way I could fill this, then haul it up on a rope. Trying to climb with it is nuts."

"Then why'd you do it?" he said.

"I didn't know any better."

He looked at me as if that were the right answer, then he said, "We can pull it up there on the cat line."

"What's that?"

"That little cable," he said, pointing. "You go on back, I'll run it up for you."

"All right," I said. "And how 'bout a safety line?"

"We ain't got any," he said. "We're supposed to have

'em, we got 'em ordered, but they ain't here yet."

"How 'bout a hard hat?"

"Ain't got those neither, but I think they's coming this afternoon."

When I was a few steps away, he said, "Meanwhile, try not to do just any fucking dumb-ass thing one of these jag-offs tells you to do. Else you'll go outta here in a bag."

Back on the platform, Marlin asked me my name and I told him.

"Well, thanks," he said. "I just kinda choked out there."

"I know the feeling," I told him. "In fact, I had a pretty bad moment of my own with that bucket. I think the fat man was trying to kill me."

"Don't go calling him the fat man so's he can hear it. He might kill you."

Reno whistled from the rig floor. He had a bucket on the cat line, and he'd started one of the engines. I told Marlin to go ahead and start washing from where we were, that I'd climb the last thirty feet to the crown and start there. I scrambled up to the little crow's nest and waved at Reno. He pulled a lever and ran the bucket all the way up.

I started washing on the sheaves, and at first the job seemed as if it were going to be purely absurd. It was a brand-new rig, and there wasn't a spot of oil or grease on it. Just a thin coat of prairie dust. But as I worked my way down out of the basket on top into the X's and V's of the widening beams, it became clear that the climbing wasn't quite as simple as it looked, that I'd better learn exactly what you could grab and what you couldn't.

At one point I tried to use a wiring conduit for a hold. It was painted the same white as the half-inch pipe I'd been hanging on, and it looked just as rigid, but when I grabbed, it moved, which put a shot of adrenaline into my empty stomach. And it wasn't helping that the soapy water was running down the iron, sliming up whatever I was trying to stand on.

I do remember how good the sun felt that morning, though, up there in my catbird seat. The traffic on old 80 flowed by me at an almost even pace in both directions, as if some secret dispatcher were sending one car, one truck, one motorcycle east, for every car and truck and motorcycle that went west. Below me in the yard half a dozen hands unloaded heavy pipe from a long flatbed and stacked it near the welders, who were working on it one length at a time.

The dog named Oil barked and scampered and made life interesting for a colony of prairie dogs whose holes and tunnels cluttered a patch of ground near a scrap heap. There seemed to be twenty or thirty of them, and they went about making their living as if they'd learned down the generations how to work around the on-again-off-again invasion of men and their machines and their dogs. Just about the time Oil got a bead on one of them, the quick little bugger would houdini into the dirt and another would appear behind a hillock a few feet away as if to say, "Over here, dope." After a while the big white dog tired of the chase and sauntered over into the shade of the big aluminum shed to lie down.

Next door to our yard, water trucks waited their turn in line to be filled from huge overhead tanks, and in the yard beyond that, other trucks came and went through each other's dust. A half-mile away, I saw what looked like Sonny's truck pulling out of the parking lot of a big supply store on a hill. Then I heard Marlin yell, "Tom, he's coming back."

The fat man was sitting on a walkway alongside the

rig engines with two of his hands. When he heard Marlin, he jumped to the ground, unrolled a set of plans, and began to study them.

Every ship needs a lookout, I thought, but I didn't say anything to Marlin. I'd scrubbed about halfway down to him. He hadn't moved from the platform. In fact, he seemed to have been washing the same four feet of the same beam for the whole time we'd been up there.

"Aren't we having fun," I said as I set my bucket next to his on the platform.

He looked at me in a way I couldn't quite read. Then he said, "I think I know you."

Oh Christ, I thought. This can't be true. First day on the job, first guy I get paired off with, and he's about to figure out that they've put a journalist in the crow's nest.

"Where you from?" he asked. When I told him, he said, "I've never been to Frisco. You ever live in Salt Lake?"

He tried Portland, Boise, Cheyenne. "Your face is just real familiar. I'm sure I've seen you," he said finally.

"Aspen's about as close to any of those places I've lived," I said. "I was there for a few years."

"Maybe that's it," he said, still looking at me as if a face was all he usually needed to remember someone. "My brother lived in Aspen . . . wait a minute . . . are you a rock climber?"

I nodded.

"That must be it. My brother was a climber—Graham Davidson. That's where I heard your name. We must have met. I used to visit him. Did we meet?"

"I don't remember it," I told him. Then I lied in an attempt to encourage the small-world notion he was working on. "Your brother's name rings a bell," I said.

"You probably heard he was killed last summer . . . in the Wind Rivers, not far from here." He looked northwest

over the hills. "Only fell twenty feet was the strange part
of it. Guy who went up Ama Dablam—what's that? twenty-
eight thousand feet or something—comes back here, falls
twenty damn feet..." He snapped his fingers, meaning
"gone."

I didn't say anything. I felt shitty having stacked my
little lie against the memory of his brother. I had imagined
there would be tricky moments for me as I tried to hold
to my bogus story, but I hadn't thought they'd be this small
or this close. I climbed back off the platform and went on
with the scrubbing. About ten minutes later Marlin said,
"I just thought of something. Maybe if we get a weekend
off one of these times, you could take me over to Wind
Rivers and show me the place Graham died."

I told him I didn't have my ropes.

"That don't matter," he said. "I don't want to climb
it. I just want to look. I know the name of the rock, and
if we went over there, somebody like you might be able to
see what happened."

There was honking in the yard, and when I looked
down, I saw Sonny pointing at me out the window of his
truck. He waved for me to come down.

"Get in," he said. "I got an idea where you can live.
You need a place, don't you?"

"Not really," I said. "I have that room..."

"Not that shitbag you was talking about? You don't
want to live there. That's the lowest place in town. You
ain't gonna last a week over there, stories I heard."

"They have my money is the thing."

"Shit, don't worry about that. I'm gonna see you make
plenty of money around here. I'll put some extra hours
on your first check. That's easy."

As we started off the yard, we met another company
truck. Sonny pulled window to window with it.

"Morning," he said.

The other driver grunted. He had on a cowboy hat and a pair of aviator sunglasses that didn't quite hide the heavy bags under his eyes. "Got another hand for you," he said. His voice had bubbles in it.

"I don't really need me a..."

"Oh yes you do. You go ahead and run somebody off if you have to, because I want this man took on. He's an experienced hand, a Mex." He nodded toward a tall, thin Latino who was leaning on a big long Ford. "Says he can drill and work derrick. Knows how to put one of these sombitches together, and I want you to hire him. This yard's too goddamn full of worms." He looked at me.

"All right, I'll put him on," said Sonny. "Tell him to wait. I'll be back after lunch."

"Now that's one drunk old sombitch," said Sonny as we got out on the road. I asked who he was. "That's the big boss. He got charge of the whole D and J operation in Westin, and tell you what: I ain't never seen the bastard sober. You see that Thermos on the seat next to him? I guarantee it started the day with a fifth of Old Crow in it, and by about five o'clock tonight he'll be pouring air out of the goddamn thing. He don't have to pay for it, neither. They give him a bottle every morning over there at Union Supply, and just as long as he keeps us going to them for hardware, they're happy to do it. They're gonna do a lot more before we're through, I promise you that. I was with him two days ago, he asked for a color TV. They didn't fucking blink an eye. Asked him where he wanted the sombitch delivered."

We crossed under old 80, heading south into the dry hills, toward nothing. We passed a billboard with an 800 number under the words HELP STOP OIL FIELD THEFT. The pavement ended, and the road turned to freshly cut, ungraded dirt. Rocks the size of human heads lay everywhere, and Sonny slowed and zigzagged to miss them. We passed flagmen and four big yellow graders.

"Guess maybe they could have fixed the road before they parked six-hundred trailers out here, but then nothing else in this town's caught up with itself, neither."

We rode for a rough ten minutes. I still couldn't see a destination. The dry, treeless hills sat perfectly empty except for an occasional rig here and there in the distance. Dump trucks put dust storms in the cab with us as they passed on their way back toward town.

Finally, I said, "Where we going?"

"Yellow Creek."

"They have rooms to rent out there?"

"No, hell no," he said. "They ain't got nothing. They ain't had a space for six months. But I got me a real nice sixty-footer out here that D and J rents to me. It's a twenty-thousand-dollar setup, three bedrooms, two baths, washer-dryer which ain't hooked up yet, but we can get that took care of. My idea is I rent you a room, which makes it a little cheaper on me and gets you out of that dump. I ain't done it before 'cause I don't want to live with the kind of low-class greasers we got around here. You...you're just cleaner. Know what I mean? I won't live with trash. I done it too long." He drifted off as if he were remembering a certain time in a certain place. "But this is real nice out here. They don't have it all lined out yet. I mean, they got things left to do, but considering what's to choose from around here, I'd say it's pretty nice."

The way he eased back from "real nice" to "pretty nice" was the tip-off. I tried to brace myself for "just awful," but it wasn't enough. We came around the flank of a squat hill, and all of a sudden we were looking down on the reason God made tornadoes: a monstrous clot of aluminum rectangles—twenty or thirty acres of them—jammed up against one another as if ugly needs ugly, as if something out there on the empty prairie just the other side of the chain-link property line preyed on ugly and was waiting to eat any piece of the huge, dismal herd that broke huddle.

We turned through a gate and under a sign that said YELLOW CREEK ESTATES. It might as well have said ABANDON ALL HOPE except that I've always imagined hell was going to be an older neighborhood than this one. The streets here were paved, and all the trailers were new. Each had a cement driveway flanked by a small patch of dirt that might have been a garden if you'd moved the auto parts and motorcycles and camper shells that littered most of them. As it was, it looked to me like the developers had spent the landscaping budget on salt instead of seed. Not a tree, not a sapling, not a shrub, not a blade of grass, was attempting a life inside this fence.

Sonny turned lefts and rights through a maze of unnamed streets that had been laid out with dead ends and cul-de-sacs. I was trying to make note of the route we were on, but it was no use, finally. There were no numbers on any of the trailers, and the differences among them were too small for me to see. I did notice, as Sonny pulled into his driveway, that there was a sewery stripe running down the middle of it.

As he was getting his keys in the door, he pointed with his head to one of the trailers across the street from us. "We got us a hot little mama living over there, I'll tell you what. Real good-looking, friendly . . . I think she's a hooker. Lives alone, walks around in one of them tight little T-shirts shows her nipples. And I seen that little truck of hers parked around different trailers all the time . . . lookie here . . . that's her."

I turned and saw a woman in a peach-colored jumpsuit coming out of the trailer across the street. She paused on the steps and bent to tie one of her running shoes, which provoked an almost whispered "shee-it" out of Sonny. I had a lecherous little moment of my own as she stood up and used both hands to tighten the knot in the yellow bandanna that covered all but a few inches of reddish-brown ponytail. Her face was tanned, her eyes were bright.

"Ooo-wee, if she ain't a hundred dollars' worth, right there, just like that," Sonny said as she got in her truck. Once she had it backed into the street, she spotted us, seemed to hesitate a moment, then smiled, waved, and drove off.

"That's for sale, I swear it is. You can just see it."

I didn't say anything. I'd seen something entirely else, but I wasn't quite sure what. Something tough, all right, or at least bold, but not the way hookers are tough.

"Great tits," said Sonny.

"Great-looking woman altogether," I said. "Doesn't look like a whore to me."

"What Sunday school you come out of, anyway?" he said. "She's a pro, and I got fifty dollars says so."

The whole trailer moved under our weight as we stepped up into the living room. "I got to get that garbage outta here one of these times," he said, referring to the smell that was coming from a greasy paper bag on the kitchen counter. He grabbed several beer cans off the di-nette table, emptied a tuna-can ashtray into the bag; then, on his way out the door, he told me to look around. "That's your room on the street end," he said.

I poked my head in and—God help me—I'd been in Westin just long enough that I thought, Pretty nice. The room wasn't large, but there were curtains on the windows, wall-to-wall carpeting on the floor, a dresser, a closet, and a closet-sized toilet. The mattress on the double bed felt as if it might have been filled with straw, but it was brand new along with everything else. I walked back toward the other end of the trailer, past an empty second bedroom, past the washer and dryer, into the master bedroom. Sonny's dirty laundry lay in a heap against one of the mirrored closet doors. A straw Stetson and a bolo tie full of turquoise sat on his dresser.

Next to his bed on the floor was a stack of four or five *Playboy* magazines. I was trying to get a look at the covers to see if any of them had articles by me, when I felt him step back into the trailer.

"Not too bad, though, is it?" he said as he got two beers out of the refrigerator and took a chair at the dinette.

I tried to refuse the beer. "Don't worry 'bout it," he said, opening both of them. "It's twenty minutes past noon. I'm thinking you could fetch your gear after work and move in tonight if you wanted."

"How much?" I said.

"Well, my rent's six hundred, and I figure we go fifty-fifty, seeing as how you'll have the run of the place same as me."

I sat there thinking I'd only been in town two days and that this was going to bring my total spent to around $650. Sonny took the silence badly.

"'Course, if you think you can do better . . . if you think I'm trying to rob you or something . . ."

"I've laid out a lot of cash in the last couple of days, that's all. At this rate I'll be broke in a week."

"What'd I tell you?" he said, as if his father had been right about college. "I'm the man puts your hours into the office. You understand what that means? You gonna *make* some money. I'll see to that. Plus, you don't have to give me nothing right now. I'll take the rent out of your first check, that's all. Matter of fact, I'll get you some advance money this afternoon, show you how it works. I'll get you four hundred dollars, how's that?"

"Fine," I said.

Sonny had another beer while he talked about the TV

set he was going to get us, the phone he was going to have installed. The telephone-company waiting list was four or five weeks long, he said.

On our way out of the park he pointed to a single phone booth that leaned south with the power pole to which it was hooked. "Right there is the only public phone out here," he said, "and if you want to see a line about a month long, you just come out here about seven, eight o'clock in the evening, when these sorry bastards start missing the little woman real bad."

On the slow way back over the long dirt road, I asked about the fat man. Sonny said the boss had hired him, that he and his crew lived in Salt Lake and drove a company truck back and forth every day.

"Seems a little mean," I said.

"Aw, don't worry 'bout that sombitch," said Sonny, hanging his lip the way he had the night before when he seemed to be talking more to himself than to me. "Thinks he's tough 'cause he was in Viet Nam and killed some gooks—he says. But I'll tell you what. I got a knife as big as he is, and I'll shove it up his ass if he don't watch out."

Well, good, I thought. As long as somebody's ready to kill him at a moment's notice, I guess I can relax.

The catering truck was leaving the yard as we pulled in, which meant that the beer I'd had was lunch. Despite that, or maybe because of it, I felt fine as I started back up into the derrick, this time on the beams and struts themselves, and the climbing felt good. When I reached the high platform, I sat next to my bucket.

I was alone in the rig now. Everyone else was at work in the yard below me, like characters in an illustration from a children's book about what people do all day. Marlin and two other hands were near the shed washing the fat man's truck. Sonny was hiring the Mexican. Reno and four other hands were rolling cable off a huge spool onto a drum that sat behind the rig engine. A couple of welders bent over their sparks at a rack full of pipe.

Two helicopters rose from behind the hills and flew overhead on their way south. I watched them turn to soundless spots, then disappear against a black wall of rain clouds on the southern horizon. I wondered about Steve, about the job I might have had. Naah, I told myself, too dangerous—flying off like that into a storm with a cargo of explosives.

The wind kicked itself up into gusts enough that one of them almost took my half-full bucket off the beam I was washing. I thought of asking for some line to rig a belay, but I talked myself out of it because by then I had worked down to iron wide enough that I could have walked it without a handhold if it hadn't been for the wind.

Sonny and his truck came back from somewhere, and I watched him drive it from man to man in the yard. He seemed to be handing out hard hats. Life with him was going to be... what? I couldn't imagine. Still, meeting him in the bar like that seemed a lucky stroke. And never say a college education doesn't count for something. The Jesuits ought to be proud. Maybe I ought to write the alumni magazine so they could include me in one of the snippets about my class: ... *currently in Wyoming in a whippy new trailer, learning the oil business, trying to drum the latinate words out of his vocabulary, trying to think up a tattoo that Thomas Aquinas might have worn if he'd ridden with the Hell's Angels....*

Ah, but the trailer did seem an oasis that was going to make everything else possible. It was going to feel like loving arms to have a room of my own to collapse into at the end of these days. I'd only worked seven hours—light work at that—and I was already tired. And hungry. The catering truck hadn't come back.

When he got to the base of the rig, Sonny stopped the truck and actually climbed out. I hadn't seen him step foot into the dirt of the yard all day, which I took to be a perk he'd worked years for, along with his white jeans. He tucked an orange hard hat under his arm and climbed the ladder to my altitude.

"I got that check in the works," he said. "You gonna have it tonight. And here... you better put this on." He held the hard hat toward me by the bill. I stretched, and he stretched, but we were still four feet short of making the pass. Let me get a little different stance... I started to say, but he gave the hat a wrist flip before I could finish, and when I grabbed for it, my boots shot off the soapy beam and pitched me, without a shout, shoulders first, down through the wide center of the derrick. It happened much too fast for fear, but I do remember—in a long second of strange calm—telling myself to get ready to hit, although I could see nothing and had no sense at all of where the fall was going to end. Then a bright flash, a terrible pain, and, slowly, the realization that I was conscious. The first thing I remember seeing was the hard hat on the ground five feet below me. I was hanging by my armpit from a four-inch piece of angle iron. The pain was in my left side, and it began to numb almost immediately.

Somebody said, "Holy shit." It was Sonny. When I looked, he was twenty feet above me and there was terror in his face. "You all right?" he said.

I lowered myself carefully and sat in the dirt. "Yes," I said, but I wasn't sure. There was no feeling at all in my left arm.

"Okay," he said. "All right... good," and then, without

looking at me again, he clambered down the ladder, climbed quickly into his truck, and drove off, as if I'd said what he wanted to hear and he didn't want to hear any more.

About the time Reno got to me, it started to rain.

4

My memory of that first hour or so after the fall is smudgy. I do remember Reno and Marlin, a couple of the welders, the Mexican, and even the fat man standing over me with something of the same look on their faces that I'd seen on Sonny's. And I remember thinking that the scene wouldn't have been any different if I'd been killed, except that I wouldn't have been looking back. They walked me to the shed, I remember that. I refused to sit or lie down, but it wasn't because I was feeling tough. I was still taking inventory. My ribs hurt even through the numbness, and when I felt around, I found a big, hard nob just above the elbow on the inside of my left biceps.

"Well, anyway, it breaks up the boredom," said a stocky kid with *BJ* on his belt buckle.

"You're all right," said somebody else. "Spit on it and run a lap."

Reno suggested that I ought to take the rest of the afternoon off and go find a doctor. When I told him I wanted to go back up in the rig, he looked at me as if he was genuinely confused.

"We get a lot of macho guys around here," he said. "And a lot of dumb bastards, too. I can't figure out which of those you are, but I'd just as soon you didn't die here."

"I banged my ribs, that's all," I said. "Doctor can't do anything about that, and if I go to one, I'm afraid I'll get fired."

"You might," he said.

"Well," I told him, in one of the most unbelievable lines I ever heard myself deliver, "this job's too good to let go of."

I did get back in the rig, but I stayed low. I worked my way around on the big beams just sort of going through the motions as the pain gathered itself. When I started to have small dizzy spells, I sat on a beam and pretended to be doing some detail work. I was still sitting when the kid with *BJ* on his buckle yelled down from fifteen feet above me, "Hey, Birdman, want to get a beer when they let us go?"

I told him no thanks, that I was moving into a new place that night. Then I chuckled to myself. Birdman, I thought. Some nicknames cost more than others.

It was about six-thirty by the time I sat gingerly into the Maverick. I put my hard hat on the seat next to me, then changed my mind and threw it up under the back window, figuring that the sight of it there would lend at least a touch of grubby purpose to an otherwise wimpy vehicle.

I stopped at a liquor store that had a small stock of groceries and bought a fifth of scotch, a bottle of five hundred aspirin, a loaf of white bread, and some bologna. When I reached to put the bag on the seat next to me in the car, the stretch connected whatever was wrong with my ribs to whatever was wrong with my arm, and the pain

shot all the way up into the base of my skull. Which seemed
to call for a little marijuana.

I rolled a skinny little joint and smoked it as I drove.
It hurt to fill my lungs with the smoke, but it was a dull
pain, which pretty well convinced me that whatever ribs I
might have broken weren't going to puncture anything.

Five minutes out of town the weed had begun to deliver on the sweet promise that has assured its cultivation
down the centuries right into my little greenhouse. Everything unflexed, settled, smiled. The long red light of early
evening was throwing beautiful shadows off every little
tuck and roll of the prairie. The afternoon storm had
moved off and was just a charcoal border on the eastern
horizon. Something dark seemed to be building in the far
west, more beautiful than threatening, and overhead it was
perfectly blue except for the streaky white contrails that
had been left by a dozen or so cross-country jets.

Even past seven o'clock the earthmovers and graders
were working the road to Yellow Creek, and no matter
how slowly I tried to drive, the Maverick bounced in and
out of the ruts and holes hard enough to make me wince.
But the flagmen waved at me—I figured it was the hard
hat in the back—or snapped off one of those mock salutes
that somehow made me feel a part of the whole grand and
dusty project.

I turned into the trailer park and made a right at a
driftwood sculpture, the only real landmark in the place,
then looped slowly around the perimeter drive. Muddy
pickups sat in the driveways, their gun racks hung with
hard hats. I slalomed around a plastic tricycle and a BMX
bike that were lying in the middle of the street, then took
the first left on a hunch that I knew almost immediately
was wrong because I spotted a trailer that seemed to have
a lawn. It turned out to be Astroturf, but it was new and
had been rolled carefully out and weighted at the corners

by large stones. An empty playpen, still wet with rainwater, sat in the center of the small green swatch, and just beside it a truck tire that had been painted white, scalloped at the upper edge, and planted with petunias. The flowers weren't doing very well, but the plastic grass sparkled, and altogether there was something brave and optimistic about the whole effect, like a bird's nest wedged into the big steel leg of a power pole.

I made two more turns before I gave in to the thought that I was dead lost. I wasn't even in the right quadrant anymore, and no matter what I did, I kept emptying into cul-de-sacs, making the slow, tight turn, then doubling back onto what seemed to be the main lines until they petered out against the cyclone fence or curved into another set of one-block dead ends. After about fifteen minutes of looking into the dumb faces of every trailer I passed, I caught myself checking the gas gauge—half-full —wondering if it was enough, which could well have been the moment that tipped me over into despair and then rage if I hadn't had the marijuana in me. As it was, I started to laugh, which hurt, which made me laugh even harder. I tried to choke it off, and when I couldn't, I just let it all go, turned the corners with one hand, wiped the tears out of my eyes with the other, and told myself to enjoy it because, no matter what, sooner or later I was going to spot that two-legged sewer stripe on a driveway and, by God, I'd be home. That would be the death of laughter, no doubt, especially if Sonny was there, but meanwhile I had sailed into the rummy latitudes where the ludicrous outranks fear and even pain.

I'd dropped down into chuckles when I rode, for the second time, past a pair of ten-year-old boys who were playing Frisbee in the street with a filthy, stiff oil glove. One of them pointed as if to say, "Here he comes again," and when I pictured myself through their eyes, I broke out laughing so hard that I had to pull over. I got Kleenex for my eyes, and when I'd mopped them, I thought I saw— two trailers down and across the street—the proud little septic stream alongside of which I was about to take my stand.

It occurred to me as I pulled into the driveway that I still had no idea how to run the maze to this trailer, but it didn't matter. I was shot. My ribs were beginning to burn and throb, my legs were weak, and my left arm hurt all the way from the shoulder ball to the tips of my fingers.

I made a trip into the trailer with the groceries and some of my gear. On the way back for the rest I saw the woman across the street pull into her drive. She got out of the truck and came smiling toward me. It was a great smile.

"I'm Monday," she said, and put out her hand to shake. I was watching her fine green eyes and her beautifully thick eyebrows.

We shook hands. It hurt.

"I've seen your partner around here, but I haven't seen you before today, have I?" she said.

"Just rented a room from him this afternoon."

"Thought so," she said. "You work together?"

I nodded.

"Just the two of you living here?"

I nodded again, and wondered where the exchange was going. She was flirting a little, but somehow there was a less than personal note to the whole thing.

"I just happen to have a service the two of you might could use," she said.

There was a pause while I tried to read her eyes. Something in them made it hard to believe Sonny's harlot theory. Then again, I've always been able to read innocence where it wasn't.

"A service?" I said.

Her turn to pause. Then she handed me a business card. "I clean trailers," she said. "Once a week, once a month, whatever you want."

I smiled.

"Funny?" she said.

"Sorry," I told her. "You did leave the possibilities hanging there for a moment."

She glanced at me as if she didn't understand, and if she'd been a little younger, I might have bought it. She looked about thirty.

"How much for your service?" I asked her.

"Let me look at your trailer," she said. "They're all pretty much the same out here, but if you guys are real sloppy, I'll have to give you the dirtbag price."

I reached into the car to hoist my duffel, and as I did, the pain danced around my ribs and I winced out loud.

"What's wrong?" she said.

"I took a little fall this afternoon."

"How little?"

"Out of the derrick, fifteen feet maybe."

"I wondered what you did to your face," she said.

"Did that shaving," I told her as we stepped into the trailer.

"Are you also dangerous to others?" she said, and padded off to Sonny's end of the trailer. The bandanna she'd worn at noon was gone. Her ponytail juked back and forth between her wide shoulders. Her ass fit her waist perfectly, and her jumpsuit fit all of it without overstating anything. I knew she could feel me watching. Certain women have invisible feelers all over their bodies. And certain men have prehensile eyes.

I shook myself loose of the pretty sight of her, dropped my gear into my room, then got the groceries onto the kitchen counter.

"I can get you a beer or a scotch, or maybe..." I

opened the refrigerator to see what Sonny had. The contents looked as if they had been snagged from the kiddie seat of a shopping cart by a six-year-old whose mother didn't want a scene at the grocery store: a can of Coke, five cans of Pepsi, a bag of malt balls, an open can of hardened bean dip, a jar of mayonnaise, cinnamon rolls.

"Looks like Coke or Pepsi," I said.

"No thanks," she said as she moved to look in my room. "Looks like the ordinary oil-field bachelor disaster to me, which means thirty dollars a visit, including the kitchen and one load of dishes. Two loads of clothes for ten dollars extra, no greasers."

"Greasers?"

"Oil clothes," she said. "Rig rags. How long you been in the patch anyway?"

I looked at my watch.

"I thought so. Well, you're not gonna want to wash greasers in that machine anyway, 'cause the rest of your clothes will forever smell like oil if you do."

I poured my Thermos cup full of scotch.

"How long's your partner been here?"

"Couple of months, I think. He's up from Texas. Been in the oil fields since he was a kid."

"Yes. He has that look," she said.

"What look?"

"Oh, you know . . ." She was pulling back from whatever she'd been about to say.

"I don't know. Tell me."

"He's a friend of yours, so I probably shouldn't . . ."

"Friend?" I said. "I don't have any friends in this town. I haven't been here long enough to have any friends. I've been here long enough to have the battery stolen out of my car, long enough to sleep in the animal pens over at the rodeo grounds, which was actually better than the miserable flophouse I slept in last night. But then, I was drunk last night, which is how I met Sonny, at the Mesa bar, and he was even drunker than I was or else he never would have hired me and put me in the derrick without a safety line or a hard hat so I could take a fucking death fall that just accidentally didn't kill me. I've known him less than twenty-four hours, but as far as I can tell, he's a drunken redneck crackerhead who thinks every woman who smiles at him is a whore, and that every guy who doesn't buy him a drink wants to fight. Other than that, I expect we'll be real close."

She stood there looking at me, hands on her hips. "Whatever are you doing here?" she said.

"Just trying to make a little money. Like everybody else."

"Yeah, right," she said, without trying to hide her irritation at my ham-handed coyness. "Well...as long as we're talking about money...you think you might want to hire me?"

"I might," I said. "I *do,* but I'm going to have to check with Sonny."

"Okay, just holler," she said. On her way out the door she turned for just a split second to watch me watching her.

I made myself a bologna sandwich to go with my scotch, but I only ate half of it. Mind and body were shutting down fast, including appetite and sense of humor. I stripped and shuffled the length of the trailer to the bathroom with the shower. There was a full-length mirror on the back of the door, and when I caught sight of myself in it, I wished I hadn't. The skin on my left rib cage from my armpit to the waist looked as if it had been flayed with a dull knife. The only clean piece of my face was where one of the Band-Aids had fallen off. How had Monday read my pathetic look? I wondered. And what about hers? ...standing there all in peach, living alone in a town full of big, horny boys, with a smile that could pick a lock. It was a look I would have hired just to hear her stories, just to know what had laid the perfect little crow's feet alongside those fine green eyes.

I washed what I could stand to touch under warm water. While I toweled off, I noticed three more copies of *Playboy* on the floor next to the toilet. One of the covers looked familiar, and when I opened it, there I was, as I always am in those authors' photos: eager, smiling, trying to look like someone you'd cash a check for. I had my beard in the picture, but it didn't seem like disguise enough, so I tore the page out, carried it to my bedroom, and stashed it in the notebook.

It was just about twilight by the time I let myself gently down onto the bed with my notebook and pen, scotch and cigarettes. The two young boys were in the street outside my window. "How long are you going to be here?" I heard one of them say.

"Three months," said the other.

"Oh, good," said the first.

Dear Suzanne . . . Little bit of heaven here . . . got my feet up in my own room in a fancy new trailer out here in fabulous Yellow Creek Estates . . . fabulous because it doesn't smell like urine and it doesn't smell like vomit . . . which means it costs a little more, of course . . . but I can afford it being as how I am a fully employed $8.25-an-hour patch worm who just spent ten hours washing an oil well from the sheaves to the dirt . . . trickier work than it sounds, because . . .

I stopped writing when I couldn't think of a way to make my fall into an upbeat event. I tried to ease the pain by turning onto my side. No good. Onto my back. Worse. Even shallow sips of air hurt. I sat again with my back against the wall and closed my eyes. Through the window above my head I heard a woman's voice.

"Shaaaane," she called, stretching the name into a

long, musical phrase, the way mothers do on summer evenings. A gorgeous sound. "Shaaaaanie...Shaaaaa-ane," trailing off into a silence that was filling up with crickets. Then, when there was no answer to her song, "*Shane! You little shithead...get in here.*"

Sometime past midnight, the sound of Sonny's truck jerked me out of a light sleep. I felt the trailer rock as he stepped into it, then saw him in my bedroom doorway backlit from the living room. He had a beer in his hand and the rest of a six-pack under his arm.

"College," he said in a slurred whisper. "You asleep?" When I didn't answer, he leaned through the doorway and squinted. "You ain't dead, are you? Just tell me you ain't dead."

"I'm all right," I said. "Little banged up is all."

"Shit almighty, that's a load off...tell you what. I thought you was dead for sure when I saw you let go... scared the living shit out of me. I know I walked away when you said you was okay, but I 'bout shit my pants right there. I seen guys die like that...*just* like that, I mean. If you'd have hit your head on the iron...that iron don't *have* no conscience." He paused as if he were remembering whoever had told him that, probably his daddy, I thought. "Never jump like that when you're up in the derrick, for one thing."

I was going to tell him that I hadn't jumped, but he was a little drunk to be getting into details.

"Tell you what, though. Any sombitch get up from a fall like that gonna make me a hand...I know that." He swayed, then started for his end of the trailer. "Wait... wait," he said as if he might be talking to his legs. "I got that check for ya. Forgot. Here it is, right here." He set his beer down and dug through his wallet. "You just sign it to me. I got enough money on me to cash it for ya."

I took the check and signed it on the open notebook that was still beside me on the bed.

"What's that?" he said.

"I started a letter to my wife..."

"You gonna tell her you fell down?"

"I don't know."

"Well, you can tell her you're one tough sombitch take a fall onto the iron and get up...that I said that." He looked at my signature. "I can't read that. Nobody read that. You saying that's your name...the way you write it? Shit. If I was a teacher, I woulda held you back on writing like that. They held me back. Tried to, anyways. Instead, I quit. Still write better than that." He fumbled with his wallet, then counted cash slowly onto the bed at my feet. "Fifty, one hundred, one hundred fifty, two hundred. There you go."

"You taking the rent out?"

"No, I ain't. Take the rent outta your first payday. I *told* you that."

"The check says four hundred dollars."

"Four hundred dollars is right...exactly right...with two hundred being your part and two hundred being my part is the way it works. I mean, if you think about it, you wouldn't a had nothing I hadn't gotten it for ya."

I didn't say anything.

"You gonna get it back, anyways. All I'm gonna do is add a bunch of hours on your ticket when I put it in at the office...is the deal. Just don't worry about it. You ain't the one getting robbed around here. Gonna take care of you. Don't know any sombitch survive around here 'less somebody look out for him. Teach you how to stay alive..." He drifted. "...believe I'm a little drunk." He ran gently into the doorframe on his way out, then concentrated on his feet and walked a crooked line to the far end of the long trailer.

I took a pillow off the bed onto the rug and lay on my good side. It hurt, but not quite badly enough to keep me out of the yard in the morning. Could be worse, I thought. In fact, it may be perfect. I got my notebook off the bed, reached my flashlight out of the duffel, laid it next to the open page, and scribbled into the yellow spill of the beam.

The feeling that a logger's chain has been wrapped around my torso . . . that a bullet is lodged in my elbow. If the work doesn't maim me any worse than this, if my crewmates don't find out I'm a writer and kill me, there's a STORY *here.*

By some accident of mercy, things in the yard were slow for the next two days, which gave the pain in my ribs a chance to stretch and travel, then settle into a dumb ache that let me work pretty well as long as I didn't do something stupid like hoisting my end of a forty-foot pipe length onto the wrong shoulder. I only did that once, and it was magnificent: The pain whipped around my torso, shot the length of my left arm, and I went down in midstride.

The kid named BJ was on the other end of the pipe, and when he saw me heaped in the dust, he said, "Why don't you catch a few z's while you're down there. Everybody else is."

Which was almost true: There were about fifteen of us in the yard, and there wasn't much for us to do. The big rig sat quietly waiting for parts while the hands loitered about at look-busy make-work.

BJ and I spent most of those two days in the derrick using a case and a half of Turtle Wax to polish all 115 feet of the damn thing. We worked our way from the crown to the base, and when Sonny could find nothing else for us to do, we started up again. I reshined BJ's work, he reshined mine.

He was twenty-one years old, he said, although there was still a lot more boy than man in his energetic face. He'd grown up in Ponca City, Oklahoma, where he'd been a star on his high school rodeo team. The buckle with his initials was a bull-riding trophy: All State Grand Champ. Summers, from sixteen years old, he'd worked in the oil field. He was a strong, stocky kid, anxious to work, and he had a natural sort of fearlessness about him that was almost entirely without bravado.

Early the first morning after my fall he'd asked how my ribs were, and when I told him they hurt like hell, he said, "I know. I've broke my ribs, and they hurt a lot more than people think. More than a arm or shoulder, both of which I've did . . . not on a rig, now . . . with bulls, I mean. 'Course, I think knees is the worst of what I've broke, and I've broke both of them, different times. Plus every finger on my right hand, and a elbow. Elbow's real painful."

"You did all that riding bulls?" I said finally.

He looked at me with his straight, open, friendly face and said, "No. I was fine as long as I was riding 'em."

The middle of our second day with the wax, I found myself daydreaming back to the Pollard twins, a couple of identical crew cuts who'd grown up around the corner from me in the car-crazy fifties in California. They owned a ground-hugging 1949 Mercury that had been chopped and channeled and painted a deep bloody red onto which the two of them had rubbed thirty-six coats of lacquer, by hand. I remembered them out loud to BJ, then told him that it felt entirely stupid to be rubbing like the Pollards on a vehicle that we weren't going to be able to use to pick up girls.

"Don't complain, we got the good job," he said, pointing with his rag to a couple of hands below us in the yard who'd been all that morning polishing a chromed set of socket wrenches as if it were their grandmothers' sterling.

"And when we strike oil," I said, "... we're going to put it in wine bottles, right?"

"Aw, hell," he said. "This rig might never even *go* drilling... if you want to know what I think. Been four weeks since Sonny hired me and started promising that I'd go out on the next hole. And he been promising Tom and his crew the same thing, and we're all sitting around with our thumbs up our ass. They can't find an oil company wants to hire 'em is what's wrong. They been putting bids in, all right, but they can't find no takers... probably 'cause the two rigs they got working is broke down half the time, one thing and another. Oil companies don't like to see that two-thousand-dollar-an-hour downtime. Word gets around. We could be dicking around here a long time before this outfit gets another bit in the dirt."

"I wouldn't mind if we dicked around long enough for me to learn what's what on this machine. At least enough to keep myself safe," I said.

"You'll be okay," he said. "... long as you know which way you're gonna jump if things cut loose... long as you never put your feet between two pieces of metal."

Both admonitions had the ring of good working advice, till early the next afternoon, that is, when I found myself crowded onto the rig floor with a dozen other hands in the punishing roar and nasty stink of the big diesel engines, on the end of a guy rope that was attached to five swinging tons of steel called the traveling block. For some reason it wasn't hoisting into place the way it was supposed to. Sonny was at the motor controls yelling at the fat man, who was standing two feet from him pointing into an open binder page with some sort of diagram on it. While the two of them went around on the subject, I looked at my feet. They were planted not between *two* pieces of metal but in the near center of a taut pattern of moving cable and chain that would have easily delivered me every one of BJ's rodeo injuries in a single stroke if something snapped. And if I had to jump, it was going to be straight backward off the rig floor and twenty feet to the ground, which was littered with angle iron and pipe collars.

It was the sort of moment I would have expected to deepen my general fright, but it didn't. True helplessness is relaxing in a strange way. Standing there with that many ways to die under my feet and over my head, I remember thinking that there was absolutely nothing to do but trust that the motley collection of roughnecks and oil tramps on the floor around me knew what they were up to and that, in keeping themselves safe, would accidentally keep me safe, too.

Maybe: There had been at least two moments in the flurry of teamwork that had preceded our running the block to half-mast that seemed to argue pretty hard against the competence of my shipmates.

The block had arrived that morning before the rig had been made completely ready to take it. Sonny had most of us together on the rig floor and was assigning us jobs when, all of a sudden, a hailstorm of quarter-inch nuts began pelting our hard hats, richocheting off the metal floor with a sound like bullets hitting an old bell. There was ducking, swearing, scrambling. When it was over, I looked up to see a welder standing on the high derrick platform in his dark mask, silhouetted against the fleecy clouds, making a dopey "Oops" gesture with his arms.

A little later I looked up from what I was doing to see the fat man and his crew rolling heavy cable from a storage reel onto the rig's main drum. The spinning stopped for a moment while the fat man fiddled with the engine controls. In the pause Marlin, who was closest to the big drum, rested his hand on the tight cable. The fat man started the engine suddenly, and the cable took the glove off Marlin's hand with such ghostly speed that, as it disappeared into the wrap, I thought—for a split second—that it was his hand. So did he, I think. He screamed, then yelled "Whoa," but the engine noise drowned the word, the fat man continued to look at his console, the drum spun, and as far as I know, that glove is still in there somewhere under several hundred layers of wire rope. Marlin went on working, one glove on, one glove gone, as if to say, "No harm, no foul."

For most of the morning I worked with the Mexican, who was doing something critical to the brake. My job was to stand like an operating-room nurse between him and the toolbox, and to hand him whatever he asked for, which was harder than it should have been for two reasons: I didn't know the names of the tools or the fittings; and Ramón's accent was so thick that even if I had known what things were called, it wouldn't have done me much good.

Early in our partnership he shouted over the diesel roar for a dirty shoe. I began rummaging through the parts on the deck for something that looked like a brake shoe. Why he wanted a dirty one, I couldn't tell. Probably just another colorful piece of oil-field glossary, I guessed, along with cathead, deadman, doghouse, and worm.

"Dirty shoe," he said again, pointing into the tool box this time. I began touching things in the box, looking for him to nod when I hit a dirty shoe: not any of the four hammers, not pliers, not wire snips or any of the dozen screwdrivers. Finally, he got his arm out of the guts of what he was doing, stepped over, and grabbed the largest pipe wrench in the box—thirty-two inches long. He held it up, pointed to the number 32 braised near the head, then looked me in the eye and said very clearly, "Dirty shoe."

And so it went for most of an hour. I listened, pointed,

guessed. About the time I thought I was getting pretty good at the job, Sonny came over, stuck his head into the works with Ramón, then pulled back, turned to me, and shouted, "Get the pickup."

"Pickup . . . pickup," I said, rooting through the tools we hadn't used yet. Finally, I had to ask. "What's a pickup?"

"The truck, asshole," said Sonny. "Get the goddamn pickup truck."

Which I did, and he fetched some sort of caliper from his own toolbox. He and Ramón finished the job while I wiped the tools I could name and put them in an order that looked good to me.

The afternoon finished as we flew the block into smooth working order despite a five o'clock dust storm, and Sonny sent us all home early.

On the way out of town toward Yellow Creek, I stopped at a phone stand across from a park I hadn't seen before. There was a softball game going on against a backstop in the far corner of the big green field. I dialed Suzanne, and while the line rang, I imagined the empty house, my typewriter alone in the afternoon light, the greenhouse. I'd tried for three days to catch Suzanne and couldn't do it. Not in the morning, not at 10:00 P.M., not in the middle of the day when someone in her office had said she was off for the afternoon. I let it ring through two batters: The first popped out to the pitcher, the second singled over shortstop.

"Where the hell are you?" I said out loud as I hung up.

I walked the weedy edge of the park toward the ball game, wondering why I was angrier with Suzanne than I was lonely for her; why every time I dreamed up her face, I saw my plants losing their stalky muscle and their green. Some things die so quietly.

A batter tagged a long, high fly ball just foul down the right-field line. As the fielder turned and made the long sprint after it, I saw it was a girl, a woman, actually, and an athlete for sure the way she dived for the drifting fly. The ball hit her mitt and bounced away. She skidded a body length, lay for a couple of seconds on her stomach, then said, "Shit." She got up wiping at the hero's grass stain that ran shoulder to knees on the front of her uniform. She got the ball and threw it on the fly to the pitcher. When she walked toward me to get her hat back, I saw it was Monday. She was still slapping at the long green brushstroke on her jersey and she didn't see me. On her way back to the field, she tucked her ponytail through the opening at the back of her cap.

I got a seat in the low bleachers with twenty or thirty others and looked out at more women in one place that I'd ever expected to see in Westin. It seemed to be a league game because both squads had full uniforms, including cleats. BIG O it said on Monday's shirt. Her team was playing E and E Supply.

Chatter from infield and bench was lively and full of the right clichés—Batta, batta, batta... be a hitter... good eye. Behind each of the benches three or four giggling toddlers chased each other.

When I asked the old man next to me, he said the score was 5 to 5, and he thought it was the bottom of the sixth inning. Big O's pitcher had a nice high arc on her delivery, a float that kept the next two batters waiting and watching a little longer than they could stand, and both of them pulled weak ground balls to third base and were thrown out easily. Side retired.

At the changeover, one of the kids behind the E and E bench tried to follow her mother to the pitcher's mound. Big O's first baseman scooped up the little girl, gave her a softball of her own, and set her back into the gaggle of children.

Big O's shortstop was first up. "This little gal can hit," said the old man as she took her practice swings. She was petite and she didn't look particularly strong, but she moved into the first pitch perfectly and drove it over second base into center field for what should have been a single but turned into a double when the fielder let it roll between her legs.

Monday stepped in. She dug a place for her back foot, cocked the bat, and pulled the first pitch foul behind third base. About the time the second pitch reached the top of its arc, the pitcher's daughter made another darting toddle onto the infield, holding her softball at arm's length as if it were a flower she'd just picked. Monday checked her swing, stepped across the plate, caught the ball with her left hand, then turned and gave it to the catcher.

"Strike two," said the umpire, a balding man in his thirties who seemed too thin for the work.

"What?" said Monday.

"You heard me," said the ump.

"That's gotta be time-out."

"I'm the one who calls time-out," said the ump.

Monday looked at him in disbelief. Then she pointed to the kid and said, "All right. If it wasn't time-out, they had too many players on the field."

The old man next to me laughed as half a dozen Big O players crowded in on the ump. For just a moment he looked as if he wanted to run.

"You want her to go ahead and kill the baby, right?" said one of the players. Then E and E's pitcher walked over to make an appeal, but by then the ump had drawn his manhood and his umphood together.

"Play ball, or I'll call this whole game off," he said.

"Go ahead," said somebody.

"We need a woman ump in this town," said somebody else.

"Let's play. Let's finish the game," said Monday. The angry knot of women loosened, then drifted back toward their bench.

"I thought maybe they was gonna eat him up," said the old man. "Never want to rile a woman with a child around. Like wild animals...if you've ever seen it."

The pitcher gave Monday a little wave that seemed to say "thanks," then lofted a ball that Monday poked down the third-base line, fair this time, and the cheer that went up from the stands and from Big O's bench was the biggest of the afternoon. The run scored, and Monday stretched her hit into a triple by sliding into third under a nice throw. She got up dusting herself off, limping a little.

From then on it was all Big O. The next five batters shelled E and E's pitcher for two doubles, a single, and two home runs. In the bottom of the seventh, E and E went down one-two-three. Both teams circled up for hip-hip cheers to each other, then hugged all around and began to gather the bats and bases and the children.

I started in the direction of my car, thinking I'd try Suzanne again; let it ring long enough that I could tell myself that even though I was the one who'd left, she was the one who wasn't home.

"Hey," I heard. "What are you doing here?"

We met with the backstop between us. She was still limping.

"Nice game," I said.

"Pretty good," she said, shaking out her ankle. "But I think I'm getting a little old for this."

"You didn't look old diving for that foul."

She shook her head. "I hate those...when it's *right*

there"—she pointed to the palm of her hand—"and you let it go. Hate it." She took her cap from her head, put it in a little duffel with her mitt. "So, you come out here to hire me, or what?"

"Oh...no. I just saw a baseball game going on. I didn't know you were playing. I haven't been with Sonny long enough to ask him. I leave early, he gets in late...."

"Whatever," she said in a way that made me feel like a kid who needs Dad's permission to use the car.

"Well...I got to go," she said. "See ya."

I watched her set off across the infield. Damn, I thought. You're going to hate yourself if you let this moment walk. Take a chance. At least get the grass stain.

"Monday," I said. She looked back. "You're hired. I'll work it out with Sonny later."

"Well, all right," she said, coming back to the fence. "I'll be there next week...don't know what day, exactly. You want laundry and dishes?"

"Laundry, no dishes."

"A man who washes his own dishes. Imagine that."

"No, no. We don't *have* any dishes. Unless you count the Styrofoam boxes they give you at the burger joints."

"Okay," she said.

"Okay," I said. "Listen, I'm on my way out to Yellow Creek if you want a ride."

"No thanks," she said. "I'm riding with a girlfriend. I'll talk to you next week." She walked away again, a few steps, then stopped. "Maybe I will," she said. "Hang on while I change my plans."

We followed our long shadows across the grass toward the Maverick through a warm breeze that was combing a good green smell out of the tall weeds. She was barefoot, carrying her cleats in one hand, her duffel in the other.

"Where'd you learn to play baseball?" I asked her.

"Redondo Beach," she said. "California, southern California. Where I grew up."

"California," I said. "I'm..."

"I know," she said before I could connect us with the coincidence. "What the hell is anybody doing in Westin, Wyoming, from beautiful southern California?"

I decided to let her tell me before I told her. I was going to have to be careful not to run my story into a corner by volunteering too much of the truth.

"How *did* you get here from there?"

"Girlfriend and I got in her car and drove to Gillette...."

"Makes sense," I said.

She checked my eyes for sarcasm, then said, "It *did* make sense at the time...to us, anyway. I mean, Sherry and I just looked at each other one day—me with my brand-new divorce from my worthless surfer-boy husband, her with her second abortion, which her worthless surfer boyfriend didn't even help pay for—and we said, 'Let's get out of this movie...go have a real adventure.' Something we can tell our grandchildren. She knew a guy who'd been working in Gillette, and he wrote that it was hard work, hard party, and that there were five guys to every girl. Reminded me of that incredibly stupid Beach Boys song, you know, '...two girls for ev-ery guy...' We made up our own words to that one. Sang it for about two thousand miles...."

I thought of Suzanne as we passed the phone box. When I opened the passenger door for Monday, she said, "What's this? A gentleman?"

"Never seemed like a big deal to me," I said.

"I guess it's not," she said. "I'm just not used to it. I remember when I was bartending in Gillette, I'd try to go home with some guy at the end of my shift...practically

have to carry him to the car then hold him up while
I opened the door. Actually, it makes me a little nervous
to have a guy do it. Like I have to act like a lady or something."

"So," I said as I got the Maverick on the road, "Was
it everything you hoped it would be up there? Five guys
to every gal?"

"It was and it wasn't," she said. "I mean, out of those
five guys you had two slobbering drunks, one gay, one
married and lying about it, and one married who was telling the truth. But we had a great time. Just a couple of
oil-field sluts. We couldn't stop laughing for about the first
six months. Guys hated it when we were together. They
couldn't figure out what was so funny to us. It was just so
different. I mean, their idea of a big date, some of 'em, was
to drive you out to the dead-dog pit."

"What?" I said.

She giggled. "The dead-dog pit. In California stray
dogs go to a shelter, right? Then they gas 'em, or something. In Gillette, they had this big pit outside town, and
they just took the dogs out there, shot 'em, and threw 'em
in. They'd just be lying there, hundreds of 'em, and these
guys would take the girls out there to try to gross them
out. A couple of guys took me and Sherry out there one
night. It was a shock... the smell... God... but we didn't
want to give these dickheads the satisfaction of seeing us
go like 'Ewe,' so Sherry gets out of the truck, goes over to
the edge of this crater, and starts pointing around going
'Benji... Ol' Yeller... oh no, not Rin Tin Tin.' After that,
whenever some redneck would hit on us, we'd just look at
each other and say 'Dead dogs.' I swear, we just never
stopped laughing."

"... and you worked as bartenders?"

"After a while we did. After the powder works. We
got hired out of a dance hall the first night we were there

to work in a dynamite plant. We were the only women on a crew of about twenty guys, and they didn't think we could do the work. *We* didn't think we could do the work at first. We had to tamp these fifty-pound bags of ammonium nitrate, about a thousand of them a day. I mean, we got strong." She pulled up her right sleeve and showed me her biceps. "Neither one of us had ever done any physical work at all, and all of a sudden we're out there unloading dynamite from a flatbed truck in a blizzard . . . toes feel like glass . . . you have to chew to feel your nose. First time in my life I looked like I got home from work at the end of a day. I think we probably went through a fifty-gallon drum of that muscle rub in six months."

Just after we turned onto Yellow Creek Road, a flagman waved us down. He had the shirt off his hard upper body, and a tan that was nearly the color of the dirt. When he saw Monday in the car, he came nodding over and squatted by her window.

"How's the best-looking chick in town?" he said.

"If I see her, I'll tell her you asked," she said in a tone that knew and didn't particularly like him. He looked at me.

"Jesse still gone, I guess," he said. "Been gone a couple of months by now, huh?"

Monday nodded.

"He's taking an awful chance leaving you alone this long, ain't he?"

"He's been taking a chance since the day he met me," she said in a way that wasn't meant to be funny. The flagman laughed anyway.

"Well . . ." he said, "I been wondering . . . I wanted to ask you . . ." He looked at me again, then did his best to put the question in code. "You aren't by any chance keeping up the family business, are you?"

"No, I'm not," she said. "I have a business of my own

these days, and it doesn't have anything to do with cocaine, or weed, or speed."

The flagman rocked back on his haunches, grabbed the bill of his hard hat, tugged it down a notch. "Just wondering. I didn't think so ... I guess I'll see you around," he said. He walked away, jerking his little orange flag for us to move through. As we passed him, he yelled, "Say hi to Jesse for me ... if he ever comes down out of the hills again."

We rode without talking. The Maverick bottomed out now and then on the rocks and dirt moguls. Pickup trucks blew by one after another, leaving us in a new plume of dust just as the old one began to fade.

I wanted to ask about Jesse, but I didn't. Monday had gone silent after the exchange with the flagman, as if the past were ganging up on her, and I didn't want to jump in where I didn't exist.

Anyway, from what I'd heard, I already had a mug-shot idea of Jesse, with his perfect outlaw name, pretty boy probably, feathered hatband, dealing coke and whatall till things got a little hot and he climbed into his ... what? ... black El Camino, and lit out for ... Colorado, maybe ... Jackson Hole ... leaving Monday to wait for him. She didn't seem the waiting type. Then again, maybe she was weak for blue eyes and a strong jaw. She'd married her worthless surfer boy, after all.

When the silence began to make me feel like a chauffeur, I tried to get the conversation back to Gillette and all the laughter. "Where's your friend Sherry these days?" I said.

"Dead," she said. "With some guy in a jeep ... chasing antelope. They flipped it."

Oh nice going, I thought. Goddamnit. She looked straight out the windshield as tears pooled up and fell off her cheeks.

"I'm sorry," I said, and when I couldn't think of anything else to say, I said it again. "I'm sorry."

She didn't answer or look at me. She was wiping her eyes with her forearms when we pulled up in front of her trailer. She started to say something on her way out of the car, but whatever it was stuck in her chest.

I wondered, as I watched her through the door, whether Jesse's things were still in there.

5

I was at the kitchen table, eating cottage cheese out of its tub, putting Monday and the baseball game into the notebook, when Sonny came in with a "Hey, boy." He threw his cap on the couch. "Writing your old lady again?" I nodded, closed the notebook. "Glad I caught you. I got an idea...what's that you're eating?"

"Cottage cheese."

"How can you put that runny shit in your mouth?" he said, making a face like he'd seen a dead rat. "Tastes like snot to me. We got any chips?"

He unsnapped his shirt, stripped it in one move, and there, centered above his soft pecs, was his tattoo: an elaborate six-color fantailed peacock posed in a kind of strut that made it look like a roadrunner in drag. No doubt it had been a luminous wonder when it was fresh and bloody; now it was badly faded, the detail had slipped out of focus, and the colors had gone mostly to blue.

He found an old bag of chips, got the petrified bean dip and a beer from the refrigerator, and sat down. "Boy,

I was glad to get the block hanging with them damn wormy sons of bitches running around out there. Ain't a one of 'em, 'cept maybe the Mex, knows a asshole from a elbow...." He looked up. "Not you...I don't mean you. You ain't supposed to know nothing, so you gonna *make* mistakes...."

Yeah, I thought. Little ones, sure. Like looking in a toolbox for a truck.

"Anyways, that leads into my idea. They're talking about hiring some kind of personnel manager in the office here in a couple of weeks, and I'm thinking why don't I just put you up for the job, what with your college and all." He smiled. "That way, I'd sort of have you in there scratching my back where I can't reach. That way, we could get it *all* lined out."

"I don't know," I said. "I'd like to learn the rig."

"You gonna have a couple more weeks in the yard to get broke in, no matter what. And I'll tell you the truth now. I think you might could make me a hand after a bit, but any ignorant fool can do that work, and there ain't no advantage to it. But, if we get you in the office..."

He didn't finish the sentence, but the way he said "office" made it sound like a bank vault in the middle of the night. I shrugged.

"You'll see," he said. "Get things lined out." He drained his beer. "What you say we get dressed up, go on down to the Mesa, have a couple of tall ones on it."

"I have to call my wife," I said. "I haven't been able to get a hold of her in about four days."

"Well now, you'd be better off doing that in town than standing in that sorry line out here."

"I'm beat, really. I couldn't go long no matter what. I think I'll just stick around."

"All right," he said. "Get your beauty sleep." He stood, started for his end of the trailer.

"By the way," I said. "You know the girl across the street?"

"The hooker?"

"I don't think she's a hooker, Sonny."

"Thinking ain't the way you find that out, now is it?"

"She has a trailer-cleaning business, like a maid service. Come in once a week."

"That could be just the perfect cover for whore, if you ask me. Real clever."

"I doubt it...at forty bucks a week."

He looked thoughtful. "Forty bucks," he said. "That's Juárez."

"Exactly," I said. "Around here it buys a little vacuuming, straightening up, couple of loads of wash...no greasers. You want to split it with me?"

"Could work out," he said. "There's gonna be three of us here come next week. Hired my kid brother Bub. He's been drinking hisself to death down in Texas. I'm gonna give him a chance to come on up here and push for me on one of the new rigs. He ain't that steady, but he's a good 'ol boy at heart, and I can handle him where others can't. Tell you what though...he gets here, there's gonna be some picking up for somebody to do."

An almost purplish set of reds was washing up into a pale yellow sunset by the time I made my walk from our trailer toward the leaning phone booth: past a hundred other trailers, through the mix of evening sounds...country music...a dinner spat...a barking dog...a child crying and talking at the same time...all of which were lost gradually to the big-base grumble of graders and dozers and dumpers that were still at work on the long, dusty road just outside the park entrance.

The line of men waiting their turn for the telephone was in silhouette. I made six, including one guy who'd brought a lawn chair. I stood in, and a minute later a six-foot-six character in overalls and a round-crown cowboy hat made seven. He gave me a weary smile, said, "Welcome to..." something I couldn't hear.

I stood for a while thinking what a stupid call this was probably going to be: waiting in the noise and the dust, God knows how long, for a chance to stick a finger in one ear while you shouted into the mouthpiece as if you were talking tin can to tin can over a string that was too long to bear the connection.

But then, my connection to Suzanne and hers to me would have been weak that night if the air had been perfectly still and the line perfectly clear. The pattern of un-answered calls had gone beyond coincidence or ordinary business, and my imagination was already auditioning sev-eral possible men for the role I'd left empty in the bed next to her. Or...it could have been my guilt at the way I'd moved so easily into Monday's gravity, the way she'd jumped into the notebook along with slightly moony de-scriptions of her athletic beauty, the smile that I'd called "...a little chunk of whatever it is that makes north mag-netic."

My guilt, her guilt...I told myself it really didn't matter. It was going to be a tricky phone call. And maybe the noise of the earthmovers, the press of the men in line behind me, would lay just enough interference into the connection that the two of us could blame it for what we couldn't say. Then again, even if we said nothing but hello, information was going to pass up and down the line. People who live together long enough get so they can hear each other think, read each other's breath.

Things moved along at five minutes a man until I was first in line. At that point a wasted-looking man in snake-skin boots and a yellow windbreaker began a series of calls. Fifteen minutes later, as he dialed for the fifth time, the big man behind me said, "Now damnit. That just ain't polite." He stepped out of line, walked to the booth, and made a hand signal that meant, Wrap it up. The man in the booth gave him the finger, at which point the big man reached calmly for the door, slammed it open, got a handful of windbreaker, a handful of belt, and heaved the helpless yellow package five feet, where it landed in a splash of dust. The thrown man got up looking like he might do something, then decided no, slapped his pant legs, and walked to his car swearing at no one in particular.

The big man motioned to me with his thumb. "You're next," he said.

"I won't be that long," I told him as we passed.

"Take all the time you need," he said.

The receiver was still swinging as I closed the booth door, which did absolutely nothing against the noise. Suzanne answered on the first ring.

"It's me," I told her. Whatever she said was lost in the noise. "Louder, darling," I said. "It's a war zone out here ... heavy equipment."

"I said ... I knew it was you when the phone rang."

"I've been trying to get you for days."

"... busy," she said. "... craziness at work ... leave at six-thirty ... back at midnight ..."

I didn't tell her that I'd called at five-thirty one morning, that I'd tried her at work. Instead, I said, "I'm dead by midnight. Got a job. Putting an oil rig together. When they find a hole, I'll go out drilling with them ... eight dollars and twenty-five cents an hour ... more for overtime, and I'm working ten hours a day."

She asked where I was living, and when I told her a trailer, she said, "Sounds awful."

"It's pretty nice, actually. Brand new, got my own room. I'm sharing it with my boss ... guy from Texas...." A pair of water trucks growled by, laying a flat spray onto the roadbed, cooling the air. When they were past, I said, "Tell me about the greenhouse."

"...Okay, I guess."

"What do you mean, 'I guess'?"

"I watered it a few days ago...."

"For the first time?"

"...just never home," she said. "Don't get on me about it, please."

"Has it been hot?"

"A little, yes."

"Christ," I said. "They're probably dead already. It happens fast when it gets hot. I thought I explained this to you..."

"I don't know what you want me to say...." Her voice cracked in a combination of anger and defensiveness. "I'm just not here that much."

"Where the hell are you then?" I said. "Where the hell do you sleep these days?"

There was silence on the line. I let it stretch, pictured her with Tracy and Joan, trading secret for secret with them. Finally, I said, "I gotta get off. Tempers are short out here. There's a guy behind me waiting to use the phone who's barely going to fit in the booth." Another silence. "Listen," I said. "Water the plants if you feel like it, or let them die. It doesn't matter. I thought they might be our connection. I didn't mean them to be a punishment. Take care of yourself. I'll write you a letter."

"Wait..." she said. A grader went by, blade down, full power. As the noise fell away, she said, "Could you hear me?"

"No," I said, which was a lie. For some reason I wanted her to say it again.

"I think we should talk about a divorce," she said.

The big cowboy tapped on the glass, smiled, pointed to his watch.

"We're out of time," I told her. "I'll call you...some-time."

"Hope I didn't interrupt anything," said the cowboy as I stepped out of the booth.

"We were finished," I told him.

At noon every day I sat in the Maverick just off the yard eating crap-meat sandwiches with one filthy hand, putting bits of my days into the notebook with the other, laying heavy black fingerprints onto the pages. Some of the entries could have gone on postcards if there'd been anyone I wanted to send them to, and when I read them now, I can still get back some of the gut loneliness I'd worked myself into after the phone call with Suzanne. But it's the smudges that bring back the real fear and flavor of the place, the oily taste of the fingerprints I ate every day off my white bread and bologna.

This work hurts. Eight aspirin before lunch...might as well have been M & M's. Hands swollen, vibrating, giving off a heat of their own, alive with little steel splinters...gloves useless.

Today's epiphany: Metal fittings don't, no matter how much you grease them. You hold, I'll pound...said BJ...then he hammered male ends into female while I held the points of connection...while I went half fucking deaf, while the vibration rang my ribs, stung my fingers, made me a headache.

Reno's advice on a coupling we couldn't drive together: "Get a bigger hammer."

Today's other epiphany: If it won't go, force it.

Marlin offered me "vitamins"...turned out to be Percodan. I thought about it, then saw myself trying to do this work through a narco-stupor...decided to go with this morning's pain over the possibility of this afternoon's maiming. "I got it when you need it," said Marlin.

I know he does. In fact, the fat man and his whole crew have taken to smoking dope and snorting coke in a rhythm that coincides with the coming and going of the white pickup trucks. They squat like Indians on the freeway side of the doghouse, where the wind has piled the tumbleweeds like a sort of hedge against the chain link. They pass a couple of joints, snort a couple of lines, then float back to whatever they were supposed to be doing, which isn't much since we finished all but detail work on the rig yesterday.

Someone put a little American flag in the sheaves which is flapping around as if to say, "Stand back you raghead bastards, here comes America," but the scuttlebutt is that we have built a ship that will never sail.

Newspaper reporter from Salt Lake toured the yard yesterday morning, with photographer. Sonny and the boss put him in a hard hat. They took him up on the floor, gave him the biggest-rig-in-the-Rockies speech, revved the engines till he had to hold his ears. Several of the hands, including the fat man, reacted to the camera as if it were a gun ... turned away ... walked away ... ducked behind pipe stands.

Reporter: The Arabs have started talking to each other again —somewhere in Switzerland—and just the sight of their limos parked together in the same hotel driveway has already pushed the price of foreign crude down a couple of dollars a barrel. Are we maybe looking at a slowdown around here?

Sonny (jumps in before boss can answer): I ain't gonna lose any sleep over it ... been in Saudi Arabia four different times, six months each, and what I know is the Arabs hate each other more than they love money. Anyways, their price is gonna have to come down to $17.50—which is how much it costs to drill a barrel of American crude out of this prairie—before things around here start to bust up ... year from now, at the soonest.

Reporter wrote that in his notebook. Big boss stood there looking at Sonny as if he were trying out for a job that needed a suit.

Fat man has taken to bitching out loud—when Sonny's off

*the yard—that if he and his crew aren't sent out on a real job
soon, they're going to twist off of this shithook operation, go on
down the road, and get on with an outfit that's got its bit in the
dirt.*

*My friend Ramón says, "Booshit." There's nothing down the
road. He's been there. People are holding on to the jobs they have
because there just aren't that many new holes going in. At least I
think that's what he said. We've worked together enough that I've
become his interpreter in the yard. He's quiet but seems to know
more than anybody here. Everyone, including Sonny, has come to
count on his technical savvy. He's up here from Farmington, New
Mexico . . . worked ten years as a driller. Showed me a wallet photo
of a wife and two kids, little girls in white dresses, Mayan faces,
like his.*

*Sonny's rented him the old camper that's parked on the yard
—no heat, no water, $300 a month—so he won't have to sleep
in his car anymore. Also gave him night-watchman duties—no
pay—although God knows what my larcenous roommate has promised him under the table. He brought two brand-new forty-eight-
piece socket-wrench sets back to the trailer the other night and
gave me one. I told him I really didn't need it. Then sell it, he
said.*

*At four o'clock most days, in the stiff afternoon wind, I climb
the derrick to watch the train go west, to let loneliness have a quiet
little moment of its own while my imagination chases the last car
toward California. Something in me likes the melancholy feeling
that I'm stranded. Sick. May have had the cure yesterday, though:
Watched a young couple—he's driving, she's holding the map—
pull their rented truck out of the westbound lanes of old 80 onto
the shoulder under the derrick. Thought about yelling, "Turn back.
The gold's all gone, and the air will make you sick. They have
one therapist for every seven people out there, and it isn't
enough. . . ."*

* * *

Today's epiphany: A "cunt hair" is a specific unit of measure. Fits somewhere in the metric system between zero and a millimeter, as in, "Bring it this way a cunt hair." Goes with a general attitude that seems to take all this machinery to be female, as in, "Come on baby, turn, be a sweetheart." And when it sticks, "You whore, you bitch, you miserable slut."

Today's casualty: One of the hands helping unload a fifty-gallon drum full of water off the tailgate of a pickup dropped it on his foot. Sonny drove him to the hospital. "I was gonna run him off anyways," he said when he got back. "We're longhanded around here as it is." Had me mop the blood off his floormat, trash the ruined boot.

Ten people a day come through looking for work. This morning, a sad old pickup, a hillbilly-looking character at the wheel, his wife on the seat next to him, and in the back, four little kids in four cardboard boxes that were jammed into the rubble of the family belongings. Reno sent them away.

Everybody calls me Birdman by now. Except the fat man, who calls me Birdbrain, which may not be as funny as he thinks it is, but there's no denying the truth of it: I am a true and hopeless mechanical birdbrain, and it isn't getting any better. If you can put it on backward, I put it on backward. If you can hurt yourself with it, I hurt myself. If you want it dropped, tangled, lost, spilled, tripped over, or if you just need somebody to stand there in the wrong place while you try to do the job right, I'm the man. Most of it's fear, I think, a creeping terror of every nasty piece of this machine, including the noise and the smell. I especially hate the parts that spin.

The war stories aren't helping: Working with one of the older hands on the draw works reminded him of a time in Rangely, Colorado. "Sombitch was running the tongs there, hooked up wrong so that when he pulled the trigger it slammed him up into the draw works right here—blap—went dead stiff, fell down and rolled across the floor like a piece of pipe with eyes."

Today's casualty: the muffler on the Maverick. Tore it off on a boulder coming in over Yellow Creek Road this morning. Felt like a piece of my tailbone had been carried away. Rode the rest of the way to the yard sounding twice as big as I look.

You can watch the weather coming from fifty miles out around here. Today, an absolutely ungodly thunderstorm rode in from the west, from Utah, as if it were being chased by a Mormon posse. Began as scattered cotton puffs, gathered slowly on a growing wind, darkened through eight shades of gray, lowered, rushed the light out of the sky, the blue off the horizon, flattened into a monstrous anvil the color of India ink at the center, dropped a ragged stem, and then, as if Satan himself had ascended to the helm of some great evil warship, the darkness was lit with lightning that danced up and down the derrick, and the air boomed with thunder that bounced the walls of the tin shed where all of us were huddled. It rained like the tropics for ten minutes. As the tail of the storm sailed over us, the sky turned gray, then light gray, then white with big blue gashes ripped into it.

Worked as a welder's assistant yesterday afternoon and this morning. These guys come onto the yard like gypsy jewelers, then spend all day at thirty or forty dollars an hour leaning into their sparks, connecting angle iron and pipe, cutting huge sheets of steel to size. Something about staring through the big mask at the white-hot spot makes them mean. They seem to have an almost tribal hatred of the rest of the crew, and they must be in short supply because they're just barely civil to Sonny and the boss. The guy I worked with called me worm boy, wouldn't answer my questions, and the only time he smiled all day was when I leaned my forearm on the pipe I'd been rotating for him and burned the

living shit out of it. Half hour ago, he went into the toolbox on
his truck, pulled out a .357 revolver, and offered to sell it to me
for $250. "Good gun, if you know anything about guns," he said.
I almost bought it to shoot him.

Friday noon Sonny caught me over my open notebook. I saw a truck coming out of the corner of my eye
but took it to be passing traffic until it stopped window to
window with the Maverick. I'd just recorded one of his
favorite lines—*"I'm a bullshitter, not a liar. There's a differ-*
ence."—and all of a sudden there was his face, the weird-
lip half-smile, that accent.

"You writing the old lady again? Ain't love grand."

I set my sandwich over the scribbled quote. Smiled,
as if love *were* grand.

"Need you to go on back to the trailer this afternoon,"
he said. "Found me a kid gonna get that washer-dryer all
lined out for us. Be there sometime this afternoon, he don't
know when. Somebody got to let him in, see he don't steal
nothing." I nodded, he put the truck in gear, then winked
and said, "Don't worry, you're still on the clock."

I looked for Monday's truck as I turned onto our
street. It was gone, as usual. I hadn't seen her since the
day of her softball game, and the only time all week I'd
seen her truck was on my way to work in the early morn-
ings. At night, every night, her driveway sat empty, at least
until sometime after the scotch had carried me off.

I got myself two aspirin, a beer, a cube of butter, and
sat at the kitchen table. Everything that ached and stung
became a little louder when I got quiet. I buttered the burn
on my forearm, then decided to do my accounts, to put
the sum of my wounds into dollars and cents.

Seven days straight, ten hours a day. The first forty

hours were $8.25 per, which makes $300. Then thirty more hours at time-and-a-half, $12.37 per, is another $371, so that's $671 gross, not bad. Of course, about a third gets sucked away for taxes, a minus $223, which jerks it down to $448 . . . still, pretty fair. Less expenses, $200 for the flophouse, $10 for the goddamn key . . . minus $85 for the car battery, makes it $153, not great, but black anyway. And Sonny keeps promising he's going to fiddle with the time card, put some extras in . . . Oh, that's right, minus $200 on that advance comes to . . . wait . . . $400 . . . that bastard took a $400 advance that's coming out of my check . . . which means . . . sweating Jesus . . . I'm $247 in the fucking hole . . . I've just paid this town $247 to break my bones, burn my flesh, wreck my car . . .

About the time I started wondering how much I could get for the socket wrenches, someone called through the screen door. I yelled that it was open, then listened while whoever it was jimmied and rattled the aluminum door trying to get it open.

"How do you work this thing?" he said.

"Turn the handle."

"I did that."

Great, I thought as I got up to let him in. Sonny's found a guy who can't open a screen door and hired him to install major appliances.

"I got it," he said, and stepped in. "You got a dishwasher or something you want hooked up?" I was looking at a weasely face with a small, failing crop of stubble at the chin.

"Actually, it's a washer-dryer . . . back here."

"Other guy said it was a dishwasher." The smell of vodka rode the words out of his mouth. I got a picture of Sonny hiring him off the stool next to him—my stool—at the Mesa bar.

He moved the machines away from the wall, squinted as he read the instruction stickers. "Take about a hour. Gotta vent the dryer."

I left him to it, sat back down over the notebook to fret. I underlined the $247 at the bottom of the page. Magic, I told myself. A rare and mysterious set of powers you were born with. Everything you touch turns to IOUs.

"Knock-knock," said Monday as she opened the screen door and held it with one foot. She swung a large shop vac canister up into the room with one arm, gave it a scoot, then stepped up lugging a carryall full of brushes, spray bottles, a feather duster. "Finally caught you home," she said. "You forgot to give me a key." She was in jumpsuit and bandanna again, as beautiful as the day I'd met her. A vacuum-cleaner hose hung over her shoulders like a shot snake. "You're just never home, are you?"

"After work," I said. "At night, which is when you're never here."

"Passing ships, I guess," she said. "That's not your partner, is it?" She pointed down the hall at the squatting man near the washer, who was stock-still, looking at her.

"He's here to hook up the washer. I came out to let him in."

"No problem, I can work around him. You, too, if you're busy with something." She looked at the kitchen table, the cigarette that burned like incense in the crimped tuna can next to the open notebook.

"Just making a note to myself," I said. "I'll get it out of your way, pick up the gear on my bedroom floor."

"Cleaning up for the cleaning woman," she said. "Kinda like washing dishes before you put them in the dishwasher...but don't let me discourage you."

I carried the notebook into my room, threw it on the bed, then buried it under a heap of dirty clothes that I picked off the rug.

Monday started in the kitchen with a sponge and one of her spray bottles. She cleared the garbage, then swabbed refrigerator, stove, countertops, sink, and cabinets without stopping.

"Got this down to a science, it looks like," I said as she moved past me toward my little bathroom.

"That's me," she said. "Domestic scientist." She got a long handled brush out of her kit, changed the red liquid for blue. "It's not that bad a job. Some parts of it I like... not this part..." She dug the brush into the toilet bowl. "But I make my own hours, choose my customers, and compared to most jobs around here, it's light work."

"Most women hate it."

"That's the difference between doing it for money and doing it for love." She hit the word *love* as if it were a handful of wooden nickels. "I get paid, which is probably the best part of all and which has the strange effect of making the guys grateful like they never are when you live with them. It doesn't make any sense, but there it is. Move in with some guy, cook his meals, clean his house, wash his underwear, he treats you like a truck... meaning... if it breaks down, he has a fit; if it gets stolen, he goes nuts. The rest of the time, he just sort of expects you'll be where he parked you. Charge him fifty bucks for the same thing, and he just can't thank you enough."

She finished the toilet and started on the mirror with blue juice and a small squeegee.

"Probably just grateful for any kind of feminine touch out here on the planet of the boys," I said. She looked into the mirror at me. "It doesn't take much. I mean, if a barmaid smiles at you, it sort of renews all hope. Guy I work with told me that every couple of weeks when he gets a day off, he hitches over to Salt Lake, not for the whores, for a shampoo. Finds a beauty parlor, lays back in the chair, closes his eyes, and drifts off to the feel of a woman's fingers in his hair. Got four of them one day. He's a shy kid, but..."

"Most of these guys are shy," she said, "even the tough-acting ones. And they're prudes... I mean it... have to get drunk or otherwise seriously fucked up to even take their clothes off. Then maybe something happens, maybe not. Flip a coin. And if something does happen, it's..." She snapped her fingers. "Talk about light work. The hookers around here charge for an hour, work three minutes."

I looked at her reflection to see if she was trying to tell me something. She was head down, working on the sink.

"I didn't think there were any hookers in this town," I said.

"Well..." she said, then paused as if maybe she were counting, "...there's a few, free-lancers. I mean, probably every girl in town has been offered money one time or another. Maybe they take it, maybe they don't. But this is not a good town for pros... I hear. Met a girl a couple of months ago, great gal, from California. Been busted in San Diego, on a very clever deal, I thought. She'd advertise lingerie shows... you're a businessman, she comes up to your hotel room, models the stuff for you, if you like what you see, you buy... the whole package. Very clever, but she got busted anyway, came up here, and the first thing she did was to look in the Yellow Pages for bailbondsmen. Said if there were a lot of bailbondsmen listed, you knew hookers could work steady. So she opens the Westin phone book and zero, not one. She worked about a week anyway, at the Mesa Inn which is where I met her. Got two-hundred dollars an hour per guy, which she sometimes took more than one of, and she gave them a little cocaine up there sometimes. Of course, they busted her, but all they did was throw her in jail overnight, then put her on a Greyhound, shipped her to

Salt Lake. But she was a riot, very smart."

"Set her own hours, chose her customers, didn't get stuck doing it for love..." I said, going for a smile, maybe a laugh. What I got was silence, then a slow turn that took the mirror out of the conversation.

"Just a girl out on her own," she said. "Doing for herself however and whatever."

"There are other ways," I said. "Look at you. Got a nice little gig... evenings off."

"You sure about that?" She put a fist on her hip.

"Yes." I smiled. She didn't.

"Not pretty enough?"

"Be serious," I said.

"Then what makes you so sure I'm not out here taking full advantage of the opportunities?"

"Wrong tools," I said, pointing to her carryall.

"Oh? Maybe this is just a very clever front...."

"That's what Sonny thinks, my roommate...."

"Maybe he's right." She grabbed the toilet brush. "Ever been spanked with one of these?" She stung the commode with a sharp backhand snap. "You could get a nice little welt up with one of these, then, when it's just tender enough... *presto*." Her other hand produced the feather duster the way magicians produce silk flowers.

I laughed. She stood there with the toilet brush in one hand and the feather duster in the other, working hard to keep a diabolical little smirk from breaking into a larger smile, because the laugh was only part of what she was going for. Just below the comedy I could feel her trying to walk me backward out of whatever romantic notions I might be playing around with. It was the sort of cold-shower technique that I could imagine had worked pretty well from behind the bar in Gillette when the easily spooked twenty-year-olds from Texas and Oklahoma and Minnesota got full of beer and started to make their shy little moves on her. Somehow, it was having the opposite effect on me. In fact, I don't think the moment would have been much more electric if she'd begun unbuttoning her jumpsuit.

"... little help down here," yelled the guy at the washing machine.

When I got to him, he was hunched between the washer and the wall, sweating like a trapped rat, trying to make a simple hose connection from an impossible angle.

"Need a third hand to hold this clamp while I tighten her down," he said.

I reached over the front of the machine while he went to work with a screwdriver that was too big for the screw he was trying to turn with his shaky hand.

"Who's that?" he said, rocking his head toward my bedroom.

"She's the cleaning woman."

"Cleaning woman," he said. "Yeah. And I'm Buffalo Bill Cody... girl who looks like that. Maybe I need that other screwdriver."

There were half a dozen in the leather tool belt he'd left on the hallway rug. All of them had Phillips heads, except one, which was too small for the screw. He took it anyway, then leaned all his wiry weight into each turn to keep it on the screw head. He was putting a last, hard twist on it when Monday went past toward Sonny's bathroom, and when he looked up to watch her, I had one of those weird and cruel split seconds where you know what's coming, can feel what's coming, but aren't quick enough to do anything about it. I yelped, swore, grabbed the heel of my left hand, danced backward into the wall.

"Whoa," he said. "Did I get you?" He looked at the blood on the blade of the screwdriver, wiped it on his jeans. "Damn."

"You all right?" said Monday, leaning out of the bathroom. "Let's see."

I hadn't looked and didn't want to. I knew by the way it felt, by the way thumb and forefinger had stiffened, that it was a nice clean little puncture—not quite to the bone, but deep enough.

"Nasty," said Monday when she got my hands apart. "Not much blood, but you better wash it out. No telling where that screwdriver's been."

As I held it under the cold water in the bathroom sink, she saw the greasy pink streak of burn under butter on my arm. "My God," she said. "What's that?"

"This morning's burn," I said. "Goes with this afternoon's stabbing."

"You're not doing that well here in Westin, are you?" she said. "I mean, this is a bad place to be accident-prone."

"I'll be fine," I told her. "If I'm not shot this evening."

"Maybe you'd better stay in tonight."

"I stay in every night," I said. "All I do is sit around and drink scotch and smoke cigarettes. I'm tired of it. In fact, I was thinking of asking you to go to dinner with me ...maybe look for the dead-dog pit afterward."

"I'd like to, I would," she said. "But I have a semi-date."

"What's that? A date with a truck?"

"I'm going to the fights with a friend of mine...."

"...just going down to the Mesa, see if you can start something?"

"No, this is organized fights. Boxing," she said. "With gloves. At the National Guard Armory. It's between two man camps." When I asked her what a man camp was, she said, "About twenty miles out of town, few hundred guys living in dorm rooms. They're building a gas-processing plant. It's the welders against pipe fitters or I don't know what. My friend's in one of the matches, and he asked me to come out and root for him. Which is why I called it a semi-date, because I don't know if we're going out afterward or if maybe I just ride in the ambulance with him to the hospital, or what."

I dried my hand gingerly, then got Band-Aids from behind the mirror. "I'll do that," she said. "Get me in shape for tonight." She smiled at me, took my hand, then peeled three sheer strips and laid them across my palm.

"Maybe we could go to dinner before the fights," I said.

"I can't," she said. "I have two trailers to do after this one." She looked at the big gold watch on her wrist. A man's watch. "I better keep moving."

She threw the dirty towels into the hallway, then picked up the stack of *Playboys*. "These yours?" she said, then before I could answer, went on, "No, of course not. But you probably read the articles now and then, right?"

"Now and then I actually write the articles," I started to say, wanted to say. All I got out was "Ah...well..."

"You're married, aren't you?" she said, as if my reaction to *Playboy* was some kind of litmus test on the subject.

"Yes," I said. "Sort of...I don't know."

"Are you separated?"

"I guess that's the way to put it," I said. "Although that word always makes it sound like animal-control officers had to be called in."

"Where is she?"

"California."

"I thought so," she said. "I just had a feeling you were from California."

"Up North, Marin County," I said. "Might as well be a different state from the beach you grew up on. I didn't have my first car till I was twenty."

"What did you do for a living?" She began spraying, scrubbing.

"English teacher," I said. "Laid off."

"English," she said. "I was pretty good in English. Got a C though, senior year, because I hated *The Great Gatsby*. The teacher loved it. You probably loved it, right?"

"Pretty good love story," I said. "Hopeless, twisted, desperate. And there's a lot of music in the words. Like water running over river rocks."

She stood looking at me for a long moment. She picked up the stack of magazines again, held them in her arms, against her chest, like school books. "Why don't you tell me what you're really doing here?" Don't lie, her eyes said. Tell me it's none of my business, tell me you don't trust me, but don't lie.

"I'm not sure," I said.

She waited for more, and when it didn't come, she said, "This is a dangerous place for people who don't know what they're doing."

"Tell me about it," I said, lifting my bandaged hand.

"That's nothing," she said, as if I hadn't heard what she meant. "That's not what I'm talking about." There was a pause that seemed to be waiting for me to guess what she was talking about. Finally, she said, "This is not Marin County. This is not school. Does your roommate know where you come from, that you were a teacher?"

"That's why he hired me. Even though his daddy told him that going to college will make you queer. I guess Sonny decided to take a chance on that part. Actually, what clinched the deal, I think, was . . . he said I was cleaner than your average oil tramp."

"I'll be the judge of that," she said as she slipped past me into the hallway.

"Let me take those magazines," I said.

"I was going to burn them," she said. ". . . unless there's an article you haven't finished."

I took them out of her arms. "Why is it that even beautiful women take *Playboy* magazine to be competition?" I said.

"Because it *is* competition . . . are you kidding? You never saw a group of guys with a new *Playboy,* slobbering and moaning? You think they're in pain? You think this is something they don't want? It's like every month a catalog of naked women so perfect they shouldn't be allowed to live."

"That's not perfection," I said. "Real beauty needs a certain offness to it, something just slightly awry."

"Sure it does," she said.

"You really think people look better with the shadows painted out, with everything that's crooked put straight? This stuff is all done with airbrushes."

"Do you know where I can get one of those?"

"You don't need an airbrush," I said, which was what she seemed to be fishing for, and just so she shouldn't think she was working an entirely shallow pond, I added, "except maybe a little right . . ." I put a finger just at the corner of her mouth.

She slapped my arm away. "Perfect I ain't," she said, then turned and moved off down the hallway.

"I'll be the judge of that," I said. She looked back over her shoulder and gave me a little roll of the eyes that I took to mean, "You wish." On her way through the living room she snagged the vacuum canister by the hose, dragged it into my room, and closed the door.

The drunk had climbed out from behind the machines and was gathering his screwdrivers. "That oughta to get it," he said. "If you got some dirty clothes, you could run a test load." I set the magazines on the kitchen table, and he spotted my fresh bandages. "Oh yeah, how's your hand?" he said. "I didn't mean to do that, I hope you know."

I told him it was nothing; he apologized again, then asked if maybe I had another beer around somewhere. He sat at the kitchen table to drink it, while I policed up the towels and a small pile of Sonny's underwear, then put them in the washer. I turned it on, and damned if it didn't start filling.

"It's a miracle," I said. "You're a genius," but he didn't hear me. The sound of the big vacuum filled the trailer, and he was in another zone anyway, sitting there absolutely still—as if Monday had hired him to make her point—lost in the centerfold that was open on the table in front of him.

Monday opened my bedroom door just long enough to set the socket wrenches out of her way into the living room. The drunk leaned to get a glimpse as she shut the door behind her. Then he folded the long page carefully back into the magazine and drained his beer.

"I'll get outta your way here." He winked. "All's I need from you is forty dollars."

Sonny, you cunning bastard, I thought. "You'll have to get that from the man who hired you."

"He told me whoever was out here was supposed to give me cash."

"He didn't tell me," I said. "Anyway, I don't have forty dollars."

"Now look," he said, "I didn't come out here to get jacked around. I done the work, and I want my money. You ain't gonna stiff her, are you?" He pointed to the bedroom. "Well, you ain't gonna stiff me, neither. I'll take thirty." When I didn't say anything, he took a step toward the washer, "Or else I'll just go ahead and rip these motherfuckers out for you."

"Hold it," I said. "Calm down. How about a trade?"

"For what?"

"How 'bout a bolo tie with a big piece of turquoise in it?"

"Shit," he said.

"All right, socket wrenches," I said. "Big set, brand new."

He bent over the box, opened it, then looked at me to see if I was serious. "This here...?" I nodded. "That's a done deal," he said.

I followed him out, watched him rattle off in an old Plymouth with North Dakota plates. When he was gone, I picked a roach out of the ashtray in the Maverick, then walked the septic leak to its source in our sumpy backyard. The breeze was warm, and except for the muffled sound of the vacuum in the trailer it was quiet. I smoked. An old dog got up from under the trailer behind ours and loped over. I rubbed his head; he lay at my feet, then put his chin on the dirt. When I made my move back down the driveway, he followed. When we reached the door, he sat.

"No," I said. "That's your trailer back there. You don't belong here." He held his rheumy old eyes on me as if to say dogs belong anywhere they are. "Go on home." I pointed, snapped my fingers. "I'm telling you... no matter what you think, you got a better deal over there. Other guy who lives here probably charge a dog like you about a hundred-fifty a month to sleep *under* this trailer."

Monday was coiling the vacuum cord as I came in to the living room. She looked at me in a way I couldn't read.

"Something wrong?" I said.

"No," she said, a little too quickly. "But I have to split. I'll do the clothes next week. Let's just make it twenty bucks this time, if that's all right?" I fished the money out of my wallet. "I'm running really late is the thing..."

I held the door while she lifted her vacuum over the dog onto the driveway.

"One of the neighbors," I said. She grabbed her kit, gave me an awkward smile, then made an exit that had all the nervous speed of a getaway.

I shut the door wondering what the hell could have driven the flirtatious maybe off her face and replaced it with... guilt? Fear? For just a second it crossed my mind that maybe she'd stolen something, except there was nothing to steal. Not from me, anyway. Not from Sonny, either, as far as I knew, unless she'd run across a wad of kickback money under his mattress or in one of his snakeskin boots ... which would have served him right if she had. But that didn't make any sense. Monday was neither stupid nor desperate, and you'd have to be both to steal something from a situation in which you would be the first, best suspect. Unless... unless the thing you pilfered didn't need to be carried off to be stolen.

The heap of dirty laundry sat at the head of my bare mattress, not in the middle where I'd left it. The ballpoint I'd left in the notebook as a place marker was on the rug. I unpiled the clothes one at a time until there was nothing except the notebook, upside down, the toe of one gamy sock caught under the cover.

I spent the next half hour sitting on the edge of the bed flipping at random through the pages, trying to read the entries with Monday's eyes, trying to imagine what it had been like for her to pick through my scrap heap of mood and reportage, of eavesdroppings, drunken confessions to myself about myself, and the Zen pep talks that always followed them. And worse: a list of Suzanne's possible lovers along with an unfinished letter to her that ended in an unfinished sentence about lying and the emotional cowardice of women. The notes about Monday herself were all runny and soft, except for one, which undid the romance of the others in a single stroke. It hadn't seemed especially nasty when I wrote it; just a question, falling in a secret place where it made no sound. Reading it over Monday's shoulder, hearing this voice through her ears, the noise was brutal: *Coke whore gone straight?* it said. *Or just marking time between cocaine cowboys?*

6

I was folding clothes on the dinette table when Sonny got home. He came in looking sour, but brightened when he saw his shirts and pants and socks stacked neatly on the couch.

"Damn," he said. "Looks like at least one thing went right today. You done a nice job here. Gonna make somebody a nice little wife someday."

I looked at him without the smile he was going for, which made me feel like a wife. An angry one.

"What's eating your ass?" he said.

"You sent that alkie out here to hook up the machines without paying him."

"Well now, I sure as shit ain't gonna pay him before he does the work, am I?"

"You could have given me the money. Half of it anyway."

"I *could* have." He got a beer, stood by the refrigerator to drink it. "Just didn't seem like that big of a deal . . . twenty bucks."

"He told me forty dollars," I said.

"You didn't give that sorry motherfucker forty dollars, did you? For ten minutes' work?"

"No," I said.

He squeezed his empty can, threw it in the sink, got a fresh one. "Didn't think you were that dumb. How much you give him?"

"I didn't give him any money. I traded him the socket wrenches."

"What? You want to run that by me again? You traded him that set of wrenches I gave you? For connecting a couple of goddamn hoses? You didn't do that, did you?"

"Yup," I said.

He looked at me with deep and genuine disbelief. "Well now, dumb isn't even the word for that. You could of got a hundred dollars cash for them wrenches from anybody...from a Jew. Tell you what..."

"No, let me tell *you* something," I said, putting the last of his folded shirts next to the stacks of folded pants, socks, and underwear. "I just did my accounts, and it turned out to be a real grim exercise. I've worked seven days, ten hours a day, and when you take my expenses out of what I've got coming, I am two hundred forty-seven dollars in the hole."

"Don't worry 'bout it," he said. "I'll get you another advance, fix you up."

"I don't want another advance. That's part of the problem. You take four hundred dollars on my ticket, give me two hundred dollars, put four hundred dollars on my account, and I end up paying the taxes on all of it. Don't I?"

"Uh-huh, you do," he said slowly. "You pay the fucking taxes. That's part of what you do for me. And what I do for you is hire your ignorant ass on a job you don't know nothing about so's I could teach you something 'bout working in the oil patch which you said you wanted to learn. Well, you're learning. I see you in the yard, and I can tell it ain't as easy as you thought it was going to be, but you're doing all right out there as far as it goes. At least you ain't got yourself killed yet. I could probably send you out worming tomorrow and you'd be okay, but what I keep trying to tell you is ... that ain't the main thing. The money's the main thing. We ain't drilling for oil out here, we're drilling for money. Anydamnhow, anydamnway. Daddy used to say, 'Just go get the fucking money ... just bring the bacon to the house,' and if I never did another thing he told me, I done that. Brother Bub be in tonight, you can ask him. He'll tell you. All you got to do is duck down, hang on, stick with me, and you gonna *see* some money. But you're gonna have to learn what things is worth, so's the next time I give you a hundred dollars, you won't go throwing it away like it was a twenty."

As Sonny's monologues went, it was a classic: a symphony of bullshit that turned on a note of truth. Somehow it didn't matter that he was a thief, a swindler, a drunk, a redneck, or that all he cared for me was what a monkey cares for a stick that lets him reach an extra arm's length through the bars of his cage. I liked him, couldn't help it, and at that moment—him standing there with his chin cocked up waiting for my temper to come back at him— I decided to duck down and hang on whether I was ever going to see any money out of it or not.

"You're right," I said. "I'm lousy about money. Always have been."

Slow surprise put a smile on his face, as if I were the first person who'd agreed with him that day, or maybe that week. "Probably don't teach that sort of thing in college ... I wouldn't think."

"If they do, I missed it," I said.

"What the hell," he said, and clapped me on the shoulder. "It ain't the end of the world. That ain't scheduled till next week."

I laughed. He offered to buy me dinner.

We ate at a steak house called the Sweetwater. He ordered a fifteen-dollar New York, "Hard-cooked, no blood," and the waitress evidently took him seriously because the meat she brought looked as if it had been worked in a tannery. He held his fork like a spike, used his knife like a saw, chewed hard, and chased every bite with beer. I had the same steak, rare, with scotch, and listened as he went on about the shit-rain that had begun to fall that afternoon when the company man from Standard Oil showed up in the yard ready to yank the one field contract D and J had working if Sonny didn't fire the whole evening crew. Sonny called the company man a piss-head, but said he couldn't blame him for being mad: catching the whole crew passed out the way he had, around midnight, with the rig drilling on its own at about half the rate it should have been making. The Standard man woke them by throwing pipe collars against the steel walls of the doghouse, then told them to trip the string out of the hole and put a new drill bit on the end. They told him to fuck off, which is not something you tell the man from Standard Oil unless—as Sonny put it—you're ready to twist off and go see Mama. Which is exactly what Sonny had told them to do when he caught up with them. In their place he had sent the fat man and his crew into the hills to work evening tour, which was going to amount to a double shift for them after their day in the yard.

"I told that ugly bastard if he fucks up out there, he gonna die and die again." He chewed for a while. "Probably should have sent the Mex with him. Only good hand I got ... if you could understand one goddamn word he says. I

can just see him trying to talk to the man from Standard
...who I know is gonna be out there again tonight, checking up. I oughta go out there myself...make sure...only
I got Bub coming in and he'll be drunk as Cooter Brown,
that's a promise. 'Course, I'll have to get drunk with him.
Gonna meet him over the Mesa." He grew thoughtful,
worked on his potatoes. "Son of a bitch lost his wife about
two months ago. She drove her car into a phone pole. They
was broke up at the time. He ain't been too good since
then is why I told him to come on up here...so's maybe
I could keep him out of trouble. Worth a try." He wiped
his mouth, balled his napkin and dropped it on his plate.
"Between you and me?..." he said. I nodded. "I could
have made a mistake."

When the waitress brought our bill, Sonny flirted with
her stupidly, tipped her lavishly, then asked me over to
the Mesa with him. I told him I had mistakes of my own
to tend to. He liked that.

"And I'll tell you what," he said, smiling, shaking my
hand. "Ain't no use worrying about it. Best thing to do is
put all the mistakes in a pile, and when the pile gets big
enough, just light it and run."

The parking lot at the armory was full by the time I
got there: pickups, vans, motorcycles around an almost
windowless blockhouse about the size of a high school gym.
I parked on the street a hundred yards from the building,
and even at that distance could hear the crowd noise swelling and shrinking in the unmistakable rhythm that's in-
spired only by the sight of two men trying to beat each
other senseless with their fists. Four police stood at the
entrance alongside wooden barricades that had been set
to funnel the crowd into a single file for body-searching
before they reached the door. The cops wore riot helmets
and held long billy sticks in their hands. The one who

patted me down was standing in front of a large cardboard box full of confiscated plastic flasks and glass half-pints of Yukon Jack, Wild Turkey, Everclear.

The man at the lobby ticket table took my $7.50 and tried to tell me something; leave and you can't come back is what I got out of it, but only because I was watching his lips.

I stepped into the back of the big, brightly lit room to see two small men moving stiffly, using every inch of the ring to stay a nervous distance from each other. Folding chairs had been arranged nearly wall to wall, but the crowd—about four hundred, I thought—was on its feet, roaring. Two cops stood below each ring post facing the spectators. Another dozen or so patrolled the edges of the room.

From where I was, I could see only a few women in the crowd, and Monday wasn't one of them. I figured she might be near the front since she had a friend on the card, so I stood on a chair, which gave me a little better view. The fighters had begun to swing at each other, although there was still more ducking and pushing and stumbling than actual punching. And what punching there was went wild or came up short. Finally, the fighter in the red trunks, a well-muscled kid with tattoos on both forearms, began a series of headfirst lurching attacks on his opponent. He'd wait his moment, bend forward at the waist, and dive wildly forward. The man in blue would sidestep, then try to catch the lunging body with a big, tired roundhouse. He connected once in three tries with a slapping blow to the stumbling man's back that sent him into the corner. The two of them clinched there for a moment, which gave them a chance to rip at each other with the laces of their heavy gloves. All in all, they were doing each other no harm beyond the fatigue it was costing them to chase each other, but the crowd had hopes, and with every careening assault huge cheers rose up over a baseline of boos.

A few seconds before the bell, both fighters slipped in the drool and the sweat, and went down. And as various little knots in the crowd turned to give each other high-fives, or to wave their fists in the air, a lane opened and I spotted Monday: ringside, on an aisle, doing her best to fend off the raucous tide of celebration around her.

At the bell the roar dropped into a rumble, and some of the crowd, including Monday, sat. She put her fingers in her ears as if she were trying to pop them. I threaded my way through the people in the aisle, squatted next to her chair, put a hand on her shoulder.

"Monday," I said. She looked at me without recognition. "Let's talk a minute." I tilted my head toward the back of the hall. There was a touch of red in her eyes, and she stared at me as if she hadn't heard. A little drunk, or stoned, or both, I thought. "Please. Just for a minute."

She seemed to find me in her memory, pulled back, and said, "Not here . . . not now . . . what do we have to talk about anyway?"

The third round started, the crowd stood again, and both fighters came out like windmills. I took Monday's hand, and she followed, with a look on her face that said, Oh, shit. When we were against the cinder-block wall behind the last row, I put my lips against her ear and said, "I don't believe this. It's like a goddamn prison riot."

"Well," she shouted into my ear, "at least there's no bullshit to it . . . not pretending to be anything it isn't." Her breath smelled like bourbon.

"You read my notebook, I know." She said nothing. "I don't know what you read, or what you think, but . . ."

She pulled back, yelled into the noise of the crowd. ". . . think you're a liar. Teacher, my ass . . . saw the page out of *Playboy* with your cute little picture. You're a writer . . . liar . . . sneaking around like a narc."

"I am...yes...because there's no other way to get this story. You think these guys would talk to me if they knew I was a writer?"

"I think they'd kill you," she said, as if it would serve me right.

"I just don't want you to think anything you read about yourself was..."

"Coke whore...you mean?"

"Yes."

"Maybe I am."

"I don't know...maybe you were. But now I think you're..."

"...just waiting for another cocaine cowboy...I know what you think."

"It's a *notebook*," I said, as if it made any difference to her. "You just write anything that comes into your mind. Nobody's supposed to read it."

"Oh, well," she said. "Forgive me for spying. Forgive me for sneaking around like a fucking narc. How do you like it?" Her face set into the same ugly little smile that had followed her suggestion that I'd be killed when my game was up.

The bout ended. The referee held both fighters' arms into the air. The crowd booed.

"Can I please meet you later?" I said.

"My friend is fighting next," she said, pushing herself away. "I'm going back to my seat."

I grabbed her wrist. "I'd just like to sit down and..."

"Turn loose of me," she said slowly, the way women do when it's going to be the last calm thing they say; and I did.

I watched her back to her seat wondering if she were drunk enough or angry enough to spill my little secret, maybe to whichever of the two men in the ring was her date. The two of them had climbed into the ring and stood with the referee, fidgeting, listening to the rules. They were heavyweights, one of them hard and tall, the other with a slight paunch and huge, meaty arms. As the ref spoke, they fixed each other with the look that tries to promise mayhem but mostly gives away fear.

I'd picked the tall guy as Monday's friend, but I was wrong. As they moved to their corners, the man with the belly smiled over the ropes in Monday's direction, then extended his glove and rolled the thumb up. But I don't think she saw it. When I looked to see her reaction, she was half a step into the aisle, her back to the ring, looking at me with an expression I couldn't read. She turned back at the bell, in time to see her friend take a solid blow to the left shoulder, which drove the crowd wild but did no damage. In fact, it seemed to focus him. He started forward, gloves up, in a measured and relentless half-step. His opponent danced backward, threw half a dozen useless punches, then jumped onto Monday's friend with a headlock that took both of them to the canvas, and all of a sudden it was a wrestling match.

As the referee tried to pry the two of them apart, a real fistfight broke out in the crowd about four rows from me, and all of a sudden there was nowhere to go. The wave of shoved bodies carried me backward, ricocheted me off the back wall and into the path of four cops who were flailing their way toward the heart of the trouble. I took an elbow or maybe a billy club to the ribs and saw the same white light I'd seen at the bottom of my rig fall. I hit the cement floor, curled into a ball, and waited to be trampled. Instead, the crush loosened enough for me to crawl, then stand in time to see an angry phalanx of police dragging four or five guys, by their hair and their belts, toward the nearest exit through a swath they had cut in the frenzied crowd.

The ring announcer used his microphone to warn that

any more trouble would cancel the rest of the event. The boxers sat on their stools, in the safety of the ring, watching the audience.

On my way out the door the bouncer said, "If you leave, we can't let you back in."

"I've had my fun," I told him.

Outside, I leaned for a minute against the hood of a Camaro. It hurt to breathe, but the good night air felt like a cool drink after the hot stink of the armory. A gang of police had the brawlers splayed against a cruiser and were handcuffing them.

I started for my car thinking about Monday—wondering how she'd done in the melee, telling myself she'd probably done better than I had—when I heard the sound of cowboy boots hurrying across the asphalt behind me. I turned expecting.... I didn't know what. It was Monday.

"Wait," she said. "I'm sorry."

"For what?"

"For being drunk enough to say those things. I shouldn't drink. It makes me stupid."

"Everything you said was true. I did lie. I am spying."

"But that's good. I mean, it scared me when I moved your clothes and saw my name right there...the book was open, by the way, I didn't open it, I wouldn't do that. But it was creepy to think you were watching me like that, taking down what I said. And it made me crazy that you were lying to me like every man in the history of the world. At least you had a better reason than most. I mean, somebody should be trying to write a story about this place. Even if nobody believes it, which I doubt they will. Most people think this stuff only happens in western movies or something. I see things every day I wish I could write down and make into a book...."

"Maybe you should...."

"Not me," she said. "I tried to keep a diary for a while, up in Gillette. Tried to sit down every morning and write in it. I just couldn't do it."

"That's the trouble," I said. "Most people who can sit down long enough to write the story don't belong inside it. Including me, I'm afraid."

"You're here, aren't you?"

"Yeah," I said. "Very much against the advice of a little voice that talks to me about every thirty minutes, saying I ought to just turn around and get out while I'm still in one piece... more or less."

"Why don't you?"

"I *hate* that little voice," I said. "...whimpering little fat-boy voice..."

"It might know something you don't," she said, in her warning tone again.

"Maybe," I said. "But that isn't exactly the story I had in mind, you know. He came, he saw, he ran like a frightened animal."

A half-smile moved her mouth. "Actually, I kind of like the sound of that...."

"Can we go sit down somewhere?" I said.

"I can't," she said, pointing to the armory. "My friend..."

"They're not going to let you back in there," I said as she started a slow backward walk toward the door.

"Oh, they'll let *me* back in," she said.

Unless they're deaf, dumb, blind, and crazy, I thought. "Can I see you tomorrow night?"

"I don't know," she said. "You got any cocaine?"

"What?" I said.

She made her hand into a gun, pulled the trigger, then blew imaginary smoke from her fingertips. "Gottcha," she said. "Tomorrow night... maybe... I'll find you."

* * *

"That's gonna be him right now...." I heard Sonny say as I squeezed sideways through the narrow space between our trailer and the huge, battered motor home that not only filled our driveway but every inch of ground between us and our next-door neighbor. It was the sort of parking job you'd expect out of a pig at a trough, and when I stepped up into the living room, there he was: "little" brother Bub, bigger by half than Sonny, sitting there bootless, shirtless, a bib of sunburn under two chins, above a belly that smothered his belt buckle...watching me through weird, heavy-lidded eyes...every mean, sour, angry pound the couch could hold. SEMPER FI it said on his forearm below the Marine Corps globe and eagle.

"Meet brother Bub," said Sonny, and before I could think better of it, I moved toward him and reached to shake his hand. He let me stand with my arm in the air for a long moment, then lifted the empty can off his leg and said, "I could use a beer."

"He ain't here to get your beer," said Sonny. "Get your own damn beer."

Bub shrugged, stood, moved the trailer on its blocks as he crossed the room to the refrigerator.

"He's been driving two-and-a-half days is his problem," Sonny told me. "He'll be better with a little sleep."

"Right," I said. "Me, too. Long day. I'm going to go pass out."

"You're smart," he said, putting a hand on my shoulder. "It's what we'd do if we was smart...which we ain't never been before when we was together." He rolled his eyes, then looked into the kitchen where Bub was bent over the sink hacking and spitting. "Don't worry," he said at confidential volume. "I can take care of him. He ain't as bad as he looks."

Good, I thought, as I closed my bedroom door behind me and locked it. Because he *looks* as if he could have been driven out of hell by outraged citizens.

I got out of my clothes, put my sleeping bag on the floor, turned off the light, arranged my notebook and flashlight, and started a page on the boxing match. The trailer bumped to the left, which I took to be Bub sitting back onto the couch. Then I heard him say, "Where the hell you get that little faggot, anyways?"

"He ain't a faggot...." said Sonny.

"Fucker's queer as Liberace."

"Don't be so goddamn ignorant, will you. He's smart, and he's a lot tougher than he looks...tell you what. I seen him get up from a fall like the one killed Billy...just like it, 'cept he didn't hit on his head...."

"I don't want to talk about Billy."

"I ain't talking 'bout Billy...but if I want to, I will. He was my brother, too. Only I didn't blame Daddy for what happened is all."

There was a silence in which I imagined the two of them drinking their beers, remembering.

"I was talking about this college guy. I got plans for him."

"You always got plans." Bub said the word *plans* as if it were some sort of family joke about Sonny.

"That's right, I do. And I got plans for you, too, if you just calm your ass down and act decent for a while... for a change. I got a sweet deal around here, and I can just sort of pull you in if you want to behave." There was another pause. Footsteps. I got ready to douse my flashlight, bury my notebook, but it turned out to be a trip to the refrigerator, followed by the sound of two beers being popped.

"This D and J outfit don't know shit about oil. They's a big mining company from back East trying to get up a well service so's they can catch a piece of the boom around here. And they got the money ... went out and bought two brand-new Cooper 750s like they was office furniture ... four pickups like the one I'm driving ... two trailers, including this one, which I pay one hundred dollars a month for, with them paying the other six hundred, plus salary, plus sidelights, so's I'm coming in around five grand a month with the government knowing about less than half that."

"What about your boss?"

"Shit. He's so drunk he can barely sign a invoice, which means I don't have to worry 'bout him reading 'em. D and J don't know how much pipe they need, and he don't know how much I order, or where it's getting delivered, and I haven't even started to take advantage of that yet. And if I get this guy in the office ... tell you what. Gonna be my final tour in the patch."

"Least you never change," said Bub. "You been promising to quit the oil field since you was about seventeen years old."

"You can go ahead, laugh if you want, but you better start thinking about it. This business is changing fast, whether you know it or not. We's a long way from those fields Daddy used to talk about with rigs sticking up thick as bristles in a hairbrush, where you just go ahead and get a different job any day you was tired of the pusher's face. It's already tightening down around here, and when this run is up, we're out, old buddy, that's it. Guys like you and me ain't gonna be invited to the next one."

"You're drunk...."

"Yeah? Let me tell you what I heard last week ... from a guy who saw the whole deal. They took him on a rig up around Casper they're experimenting with ... run entirely on computers."

"That's just bullshit. They're always gonna need crew...."

"Oh, they got a crew all right. And every son of a bitch on it, which includes one woman, has a college degree, just like that guy in there. You understand? This is the last boom for you and me, little brother. And if you don't want in on what I got going, you just remember I told you...."

There was a heavy pounding on the door. I slung the flashlight under the bed, covered the notebook with my body, and had a moment of horrible fear before I realized that it was the front door that was under assault. Sonny answered it, and before he could speak, someone was yelling at him. "...second night in a row you bastard...get out here...wormy fuckheads burned the engine up this time...and where the hell were you? You don't even have a goddamn phone, so I have to drive all the way in here to find your goddamn truck to even know where you're living while number sixteen sits down losing about thirteen hundred dollars an hour of Standard Oil money...."

"Let me get my boots on," said Sonny. "What did they burn up?"

"How the fuck do I know?" came the voice that was yelling every word. "That's your job, pusher. And whatever it is, we ain't paying for it, you hear? And if that rig is down for more than four hours tonight, you can just take it off the hole and drive it home. You got that? Four hours ...I'm coming out there, and if that rig isn't drilling ahead, you and your whole wormy outfit can just twist off...."

"I got it," said Sonny. "I got it. We'll have her up."

"Four hours," the company man yelled again from the end of the driveway. I opened my door to see Sonny gathering his things, Bub pulling on his boots.

"Listen," Sonny said, pointing at me. "Get your pants on. I need you to drive into the yard, get the Mex...call

Reno...his number's right by the time cards...tell him to bring his truck, then I want all three of you out at number sixteen as fast as you can get there. Gonna maybe need you run a shuttle for parts. Tell Reno we probably got burned-up bearings."

I remember worrying that I was going to kill the Maverick the way I pushed it through the dark over Yellow Creek Road toward town. The moon was down and I'd lost a headlight, but it was past midnight, so I had both sides of the wide roadbed to myself. The mud that was left from that afternoon's thunderstorms had taken the usual pound and jar out of the ride and replaced it with a more forgiving sort of shush and fishtail, which the poor old car was handling pretty well. Just keep your foot on it, I told myself. This is a night for the accelerator, not the brakes.

Actually, I could have used a little more brake at the yard entrance. As it was, I slid sideways into the chain-link gate at about ten miles an hour, then sat there honking for Ramón. He appeared out of the back of Sonny's camper, buckling his belt, combing his hair with his hands. I told him what had happened as he unlocked the gate. He asked me to say it again, slower, and when I did, he shook his head, said, "Chihuahua," then let me into the tin shed to phone Reno. He answered on the fifth ring, listened, and said he'd pick us up in ten minutes.

While we waited, I parked the Maverick on the yard, got my down jacket out of the trunk, thought about putting on an extra pair of socks. There was no telling how long we were going to be out on the prairie wherever the hell number 16 was, and my feet were already starting to feel small and hard. Ramón visited the camper and came back wearing an insulated jumpsuit and a stocking cap under his hard hat.

"Too cold. Too many stars," he said, as if his Mayan soul knew some formula for counting cosmic dots, then dividing by something to come up with the chill factor.

"No moon, either," I said, as if that ought to be in the equation somewhere, as if I knew squat about the night sky.

Reno bucked onto the yard driving one of the company pickups. When he had it backed against the double door on the tin shed, he asked me to tell him again exactly what the company man had said about the trouble. When I finished, he looked at Ramón and said, "Could be the brake." Ramón nodded, and the two of them loaded some tools and a couple of machines I didn't recognize.

On our way through the gate Ramón opened the passenger door as if to climb out, except that Reno didn't stop. Ramón pulled the door shut, then said, "We should lock the gate, yes?"

"Forget it," said Reno. "The worst thieves around here have keys."

The way back over Yellow Creek Road was rougher in the truck than it had been in the Maverick. I watched the stars out the windshield to try to take my mind off my suffering ribs. As we turned south past the trailer park, a fingernail moon rose over the black silhouette of the Uintas, and the graded road petered away to wheel marks with a ridge of prairie scrub growing between them. Reno slowed as we drummed over a cattle guard, then settled back into the slippery track. Rabbits ditched in and out of our high beams like huge crickets, and with every hill we skirted, the darkness seemed to lower and close.

After about half an hour Ramón looked at his watch.

"It's not far," said Reno. Then he looked at me. "Sonny take anybody else with him?"

"His brother Bub," I said. "He got in from Texas tonight."

"Yeah. I met him at the Mesa. Sonny said he was hiring him, except there ain't no job for him... 'less Sonny runs somebody off. The two of them were 'bout half drunk when I saw 'em."

"They sobered up pretty fast when the company man came storming in on us," I said.

"I'll bet they did," he said. "Anyways, I hope they did, because if Standard pulls this job, we're all going to be looking for work come morning."

We slowed to splash across a shallow creek and as we bucked toward higher ground, I spotted a foggy yellow glow leaking into the sky from the backside of the hill we were flanking. Then the topmost derrick light jumped into view, then the whole lit derrick and the flat pad that had been cut from the hillside to accommodate the lonely operation. Three pickups sat at the base of the rig, their headlights aimed at its huge motor. Two men were on the machine itself, using a small sledge on the handle of a long wrench. Five others stood in a tight semicircle below them, breathing steam into the cold air.

We parked on the edge of a rectangular pit that could have been a catfish pond if it hadn't been full of oil. On my way out of the truck I stumbled over the pipes that connected it to the rig and had to make a two-handed, stiff-arm, body-bridge save to keep from going facedown into the greasy mud at the diked edge of the nasty little lake. I was shaking my hands, trying to fling the worst of the sludge off, when Ramón said, "No swimming tonight," and threw me a rag out of the back of the truck. I blackened it, then found another and blackened it, then gave up.

"Sombitch is fused on there," said Sonny as Reno and Ramón and I joined the fat man's crew to watch. Bub took a last swing at the wrench, looked at Sonny, shook his head.

"Let me try it," said the fat man.

"Just stay right where you are," said Sonny. "You done enough for tonight."

"She burned up?" said Reno.

"I don't think so," said Sonny. "Don't smell like it, anyways."

"It just locked up is all," said the fat man.

"That's 'cause you tried to pull up off the bottom without..."

"The hell I did, now..." said the fat man. "All I done was..."

"All you done was drive it like a fool," said Sonny. "And I oughta run your ass outta here for it." The fat man started to say something, but swallowed it. His crew stood with their hands in their pockets, looking at the ground. Bub watched the whole group from above, a hammer in his hands.

Reno and Ramón got onto the catwalk with the brothers and looked into the naked works. They talked, then Sonny sent Ramón to our truck for some sort of hydraulic jacking device that they attached to the nub of what looked like an axle among the gears. Reno pumped the jack handle till he could barely move it. Bub took over and put another ten strokes on it, then stopped and shook his head. "Fucker's deep-froze in there," he said.

Ramón pointed to the biggest of the gear wheels and pantomimed a half-turn for it. "Might work," said Sonny; then he climbed a ladder onto the floor, to the controls.

I put at least fifteen feet between myself and the rig as the huge engine fired, and even so, I wanted to plug my ears. I didn't, because nobody else did. Not that it would have done any good to plug my ears against the awful roar, the way it came after my whole body, turned it into a drum, shook my bones and my blood, frightened me and filled me with an almost chemical sort of rage all at the same time. Meanwhile, Reno and Bub and Ramón stood there on the machine's little catwalk—a foot from its open heart—as if the beast were purring.

Marlin walked over, stood next to me, said something. I pointed to my ears and made a signal that meant Kablooie. He leaned closer and shouted, "...don't think anybody knows what the hell they're doing around here."

Reno came down off the catwalk and told the fat man and the rest of his crew to stand aside. Marlin and I were far enough out that he didn't say anything to us, and we stood where we were. Bub and Ramón left the jack where it was and stepped out of the face of the machinery. Sonny waved, then dropped the engine into gear. The motor strained, the rig shuddered, the pipe stands hanging in the derrick rattled, something snapped, and the steel bar they had been working to free exploded out of the guts of the machine and harpooned fifteen feet straight into Marlin's chest. There was a dull thud as the bar bounced, then fell away into the mud. Marlin went onto his back without a sound, eyes wide and fixed desperately on me. I got onto my knees next to him and almost immediately felt hands on the scruff of my jacket as someone threw me out of the way. When I got a look, the fat man was kneeling where I had knelt, breathing steam into Marlin's eerie stare.

The engine noise died into a terrible quiet as Marlin's crewmates scrambled to him. Reno arrived just behind them, shouldered in, got to one knee, then said, "All right, all right... he's alive... don't touch him yet." The fat man rocked back on his haunches, picked the steel bar out of the mud, looked at it, then stood and screamed, "Sons of bitches... motherfucking sons of motherfucking bitches..."

Sonny stopped halfway down the rig steps when he

saw the fat man turn and cock his arm, then whip the
heavy bar through the air straight at him. The strength of
the throw was unbelievable. It missed, but came in hard
enough to ricochet off the steel stairs behind Sonny and
into his hip. He hugged the handrail to keep his feet, and
when he looked, the fat man was still coming. Bub vaulted
from the catwalk with the little sledge in his hand. "Come
on, cocksucker," he said, as if things were just getting good.
"You want some of this . . . you want to dance?"

The fat man stopped, looked at the two of them. Bub
was smiling. Sonny pulled his sheath knife. "That's it, asshole," he said. "You're run off, you hear? This whole motherfucking mess is your fault, and I want you the fuck outta
here. You go ahead and get that man to the hospital, then
drop that truck off in the yard and get back to Salt Lake
any way you can, I don't care how. You hear me?"

The fat man stood perfectly still.

"I mean it, now," said Sonny. "I ain't gonna fuck with
you no more. Just get on down the road. And don't try to
take that truck, 'cause if it ain't sitting in the yard by noon,
I swear I'll have the goddamn highway patrol run your ass
down."

All of us had frozen where we had been when the fat
man threw the steel, and all of us were still frozen as the
three of them stood there, one with a hammer, one with
a knife, and one in a rage that might well have been up
to both.

"For chrissakes, this man's hurt bad," Reno shouted.

The fat man looked at the group huddled over Marlin,
then turned back and pointed at Sonny. "You and I ain't
finished," he said.

". . . unless you want this up your ass," said Sonny,
shaking his knife, but the fat man had already started for
the truck.

Marlin had begun to shiver badly, and his eyes had

closed. I stood and felt my own shakes, felt the blood rush to my head and had to sit again. I crawled back into the group about the time Ramón came from one of the trucks with two blankets. Then all of us lifted Marlin, wrapped him, and set him gently back into the mud.

The fat man backed the pickup to us. There was a discussion as to whether Marlin would be better off in the front seat or stretched out in the cargo bed, in the cold.

"His chest is probably caved," said Reno. "I don't know about sitting him up."

"Just get out the way," said the fat man, then lifted Marlin as if he were a sleeping child, carried him to the cab, and slumped him onto the seat. The rest of his crew were barely into the bed of the truck by the time the fat man gunned the engine, threw two muddy rooster tails, gained the road, and disappeared around the hillside.

"He gonna be all right?" Sonny asked Reno when he and Bub reached us.

"I don't know," said Reno. "Pretty bad."

"Damn," said Sonny. "I waved everybody out of the way."

"Don't worry 'bout it," said Bub. "Ain't your fault if these sombitches is too wormy to keep their eyes on the driller..."

That was it for me. Fear gave way to fury, and fury spoke. "Fuck you," I said, then heard what I'd said and didn't care. "Just fuck you. You can't bring us out here and kill us, goddamnit, and then tell us we have to watch the driller. What about the driller watching us?"

"Calm down..." said Sonny.

"You little fairy..." said Bub, as the surprise on his face went to anger.

"Hold it," yelled Sonny, grabbing his brother by the forearms, looking him in the eyes, the way older brothers can. "You was out of line on that one and I want you to leave off, right now," he told him. "You and Reno and the Mex get over there and find that shaft. We still got to put this thing back together. Go on, do it."

As the three of them walked toward the rig, Sonny took my arm and walked me toward the trucks. "Listen," he said. "I want you to know I *was* watching you. I saw the two of you there, and I knew that thing was maybe gonna let go, but I thought you was far enough back, I swear I did. It's the kind of thing you can't always tell. You know what I mean?"

I didn't answer him.

"I'm sorry about what happened," he said. "I couldn't show it with Tom going crazy and all, but I hate to see anybody hurt. But these things do happen. This ain't tiddleywinks. Men get hurt. But we'll see he gets took care of, don't worry 'bout that." He put a hand on my shoulder. "You all right?" he said.

"I have to get out of here," I said. "That could have been me that was hit. Almost *was* me, for chrissakes. It's like everything here, including half the crew, is waiting to jump up and kill somebody. I don't know, maybe this is just the way it goes in the oil field, and if it is, I swear to God I don't know how you stand it. How anybody stands it."

"You ain't gonna quit on me, are you?" he said. "I need you right now."

"Sonny," I said. "This is crazy for me. I don't belong here."

"Nobody belongs here," he said. "It's just a place you end up at. And as long as we're here, we got to help each other . . . is all I'm asking."

"I'm sorry, I can't do this," I told him.

"I don't need you for this," he said, pointing to the rig. Reno and Bub and Ramón were back on the catwalk, pulling parts from the motor. "We'll get this lined out, no problem. What I need you to do is drive into the yard and make some calls. Want you to phone the hospital, see how that boy's doing, then call up the boss and tell him what happened. You can do that, can't you?" I nodded. "And tell the boss we'll have this thing up and drilling by the time the morning tour gets here. Then you wait on the yard till the other hands get in, tell 'em just sit tight."

I killed three rabbits on my long way back over the ragged dirt track toward town. I told myself it couldn't be helped. I was working against the kind of fatigue that follows a deep scare, using what small focus I had left to hold the road, and to remind myself that I wasn't safe yet ... that the awful worst usually happens away from the crux ... that calamity is a sniper, that you never hear the shot that kills you ... that every time I'd braced myself against the promise of violence—whether it was hanging by chains and cables over my head or getting a mean drunk on the stool next to me—nothing had happened ... that while I watched the boxers, a fight broke out in the audience.

The image of Marlin going down like an arcade target played over and over for me: the look in his bewildered eyes as he lay there in the mud, his hands still in his pockets. You're all right as long as you have the fear on you, I told myself. Remember Marlin's brother, the man who climbed El Capitán, the Towers of Paine, and Ama Dablam, then came home to die on a weekend trip up easy rocks in Wyoming. Remember your own long, dreamy fall through the center of the derrick, the one that began as you reached for a hard hat. Don't relax ... don't get careless ... this ain't tiddleywinks ... nobody belongs here ... and now you know, don't you, what kind of ship would sign your sorry ass aboard....

It was the sort of babble that gets loose in your head

when you've just been shot at and missed: a weird, jumbled reverie full of pictures and voices that are most of what I remember of the ride. That and the rabbits, which began to stand for everything that night, with their damned rabbit eyes, frozen in my high beams, staring straight at me as if they couldn't believe that in all the wide darkness of the open prairie this truck, this desperate pair of headlights, had found them.

First light was turning to pale halo over the eastern hills by the time I pulled through the open yard gate. I used the keys Sonny had given me to let myself into the big shed, found the boss's number, and dialed it. While it rang, I rehearsed a short version of the evening: We had a man hurt out on number 16 tonight...Sonny thinks you ought to go by the hospital...but he says don't worry, they'll have the rig fixed by the time the day crew comes on.

When there was no answer, I called Information, then the hospital. I asked the woman who answered if they'd admitted an oil-rig injury.

"Name?" she said.

"I only know his first name, Marlin," I told her. There was a long pause.

"You have no last name at all?" she said.

"No, I don't," I said, "but come on. How many rig casualties can there have been tonight?"

"Three," she said, in an almost bored tone.

Chest injury, I told her. Probably brought in within the last hour. She put me on hold again. "Who are you?" she said when she came back on the line.

"A friend," I said. "I'm with the same company. I was there when it happened."

"Well," she said, "the doctor's still with him, but it looks like a crushed sternum, maybe a collapsed lung. We're trying to arrange a life flight for him to Salt Lake."

"Is he going to make it?" I asked.

"Critical, but stable," she said.

"What about the men who brought him in?" I asked her.

"They left when I called the police," she said. "The big one threatened the doctor. He seems to have a mental problem."

I tried the boss again, and when there was still no answer, I walked back to the truck, started the engine for heat, lay across the seat, and slept.

7

I woke to BJ's sunny face at the driver's side window.

"Birdman," he said. "How'd you get promoted into a truck?"

I looked at my watch. It was a little after seven. I rolled the window down and told him the story. When I got to the part about Marlin, BJ took a step backward and said, "Fuck all, man. I've broke my sternum. That's a bad one."

Other hands arrived, drifted over. They listened to the story as if they'd heard it before: rig down, man hurt, a face-off with hammers and knives, a whole crew sent packing...just another day at the office, just another violent night in the middle of nowhere drilling for oil. At one point BJ even found the silver lining. "Sonny's gonna need new crew out there tonight, for sure. Maybe we'll get some real work around here," he said.

The catering truck arrived, and most of us walked over for coffee.

"Where's Tom now?" said one of the hands.

"I don't know," I said. "Last report, from the nurse

at the hospital, he was still in a rage. Sonny told him to drop the truck off or he'd have him arrested. I don't know if he'll show or not."

"Oh, he'll be here," said BJ. "It's payday."

Payday. I'd lost track completely.

The boss's truck came onto the yard. When he saw the bunch of us idling at the lunch truck, he drove over and barked out the window at us. "Having a tea party, are we?" He looked as if he hadn't slept, as if sleep wouldn't have done him any good anyway.

"There's been some trouble...." I said.

"There's gonna be trouble all right. Where the hell's Reno, where's Sonny...?"

"Out on number sixteen," I said. "We had a man hurt last night. Pretty bad, I think. The rig went down. We went out to fix..."

"What the hell you mean, the rig went down?" he said.

I was about to say, I don't know what the fuck I mean, you fucking drunk, and what about the *man*, when a company truck splashed onto the yard with Sonny, Bub, and Reno in the front seat. Ramón was in the back. They parked next to the shed. The boss threw his truck into gear and stormed it over to them.

For the next five minutes we watched as Sonny stood by the boss's window making large gestures, appealing to Reno for witness, yelling sometimes, listening while the boss yelled at him.

I was getting a second cup of coffee when a small plane lifted out from behind the northern hills, banked west, and climbed into the bright sky. I thought it might be Marlin; hoped it was.

The boss finished whatever he was saying to Sonny, threw a bundle of envelopes at him, then spun his truck into a wide U-turn. He came out of it near the gate, then stood hard on the brakes just in time to make a skidding nose-to-nose stop with the last of the company pickups.

The fat man sat motionless behind the wheel, staring at the boss through the mud-splattered windshield. What was left of his crew piled out of the truck and backed away as if it were ticking.

The boss waved his arm, meaning, Back it out, then he honked his horn, which made me think he didn't quite understand the awful promise of the moment. I did, and found myself looking around for cover, something to duck under or behind if the yard all of a sudden turned into the OK Corral.

The boss threw his gearshift into park, flung open his door, then walked to the fat man's passenger window, where he made another angry move-it gesture, and started to yell something. Whatever it was, he didn't get to finish it, because the fat man hit the gas, blew the boss off the door, smashed forward into the empty truck in front of him, then shuddered it straight back across the yard till steam burst from his radiator and the engine died.

There was a stunned silence. Sonny broke it by yelling at Reno to call the cops. The fat man made several tries to restart the stalled pickup, then climbed out, glanced slowly around the yard at all of us, then faced the brothers with a look that was beyond anger, beyond fear, full of the kind of insanity that has no heat, that seems to be coming up out of the quiet eye of a terrible storm that's about to break.

Sonny pulled his knife, and Bub picked up a gnarly piece of angle iron, but neither of them looked like he wanted this round.

"You might as well just back off 'fore it gets any worse," said Sonny, but there was no authority to it, none of the hot blood that had seen him through the first stand-off. Then, as if his knife had begun to feel a little small under the circumstances, he added, "The cops is on their way."

The fat man got a small, tight smile around his mouth. This is it, I thought. The streets of Laredo. *Gunsmoke* without the guns...but it wasn't. Incredibly, the fat man turned quietly and walked for the gate, almost sauntered. I couldn't believe it. I don't think anybody else believed it, either, because no one moved a step. Except the boss, who gave the fat man wide berth as he strolled calmly through the gate and off the yard.

Maybe he's going to get a gun, I thought as we watched him disappear among the heavy equipment that was parked in the yard next door to ours.

"Did I miss something? Is it over?" said BJ.

"Looks like it," I said.

"Don't *feel* like it," he said.

A relieved sort of milling took up among the hands around the coffee wagon. Ramón walked past on his way to the camper, shaking his head. Sonny holstered his knife, and Bub dropped the angle iron; then the two of them met the boss at the crumpled trucks.

"...least now you see what I'm dealing with," Sonny said.

The boss gave him a disgusted look. "Just get one of these trucks running so I can get over to Standard and clean up your mess," he said.

About the time the brothers got the hood up, a police cruiser rolled into the yard without lights or siren. The boss waved it over, then squatted at the driver's door and spoke to the young cop behind the wheel. Sonny bent into the conversation with his two cents; then, exactly as the two of them stood to point to the yard next door, a diesel revved somewhere among the parked earthmovers, and the biggest of the yellow bulldozers backed and turned and began a heavy crawl for the fence.

There were shouts of "Holy shit," and "Oh my fucking God," as the huge cat folded the chain link like chicken wire under its treads, then took an angle for Sonny's camper. Ramón had one foot on the rear step and the other in the camper before he realized the full lumbering truth of the moment. He jumped free just as the teeth of the bucket pierced the tinny shell, then smeared it sideways off the bed of the truck.

The cop used his radio, unracked the riot gun on his dashboard, and stood out of the car to watch with the rest of us as the fat man lifted the dozer's shovel and dropped it on the cab of Sonny's truck.

"Shoot him," yelled Sonny, "shoot the fucker." The cop took a step out from behind his cruiser, then took it back as the big machine swung in our direction, snorted black smoke, and rolled straight at us.

We scattered like rats. I ran a wide arc to the rig and scrambled up onto the floor with Ramón. Others made for the gate, where the catering truck almost ran them down on its panicked way out of the yard. Reno and the boss headed for the shed, along with BJ and the fat man's orphaned crew.

Sonny and Bub were the last to move. The cop peeled out in reverse, which left the brothers between the dozer and the dead company trucks, where, for one dumb moment, they stood like rodeo clowns over a downed cowboy, waiting for the big yellow bull to veer. Sonny broke first, then Bub in the other direction, and a second later the fat man slammed the dozer full-on into both trucks, shattering the windshields, blowing the front tires, crushing the hoods. Then he backed up, raised the bucket, and began some brutal detail work on the boss's truck.

There were sirens from two directions as three more police cars converged on the gate and skidded in next to the cop who had answered the first call. They talked while the fat man destroyed the second pickup. As he did, Bub circled in from the side and tomahawked a big wrench into the driver's cage of the cat. The fat man ducked, then turned the machine toward Bub, who took off in a bow-legged run for the shed.

When the police had a plan, six of them walked through the gate in a loose phalanx, riot helmets on, visors down, shotguns pointed into the air. They stopped when the fat man disengaged from the ruined trucks and headed for a fresh one, the last of the company pickups, the one I had driven onto the yard and parked next to the shed. As he went to work on it, the nervous police formed a wide horseshoe around the machine, and one of them used a bullhorn. Whatever he said was lost in the noise of the last truck's slaughter and the ripping of the aluminum shed wall. Finally, at a signal from the cop with the bullhorn, one of the officers got to one knee and lowered the barrel of his gun.

It was a strange moment because, in a way, from the time I'd gained my safety on the rig floor, I'd felt myself rooting for the fat man, liking him, admiring the justice of his rampage, hoping that before they figured out how to stop him, he'd pound every D and J vehicle to scrap and leave the whole dangerous, drunken, sloppy operation out of business.

Now it looked like they were going to shoot him. Not that he seemed to care. The sight of the police and their guns hadn't broken his workmanlike concentration at all. He finished the third company truck while the cop with the bullhorn issued a last warning, then he turned his cool fury to the demolition of the shed itself.

I winced as the shot went off, saw the shooter duck

backward out of the hail of pellets that ricocheted over him off the engine block. Whatever was hit, it was a kill shot: One diesel cough and the dozer went dead ... bucket frozen in the air ... dangling an unfinished mouthful of aluminum paneling.

The fat man was the first to move: Slowly, carefully, he took off his hard hat, hung it on a gear lever, leaned back in his seat, looked at the guns, then around the yard at ruins of the company fleet. Then he smiled. Miller time.

The police spent the next hour or so taking statements. I included the rig drama of the night before in my version, but the cop with the clipboard didn't seem interested. Did the fat man say anything before he went for the dozer, he wanted to know; did he threaten anybody? Not a word, I told him; he went about his rampage with a kind of calm that was the most frightening thing about it ... you guys saw it when he lay facedown and put his hands behind his back for the cuffs ... no struggle ... no resistance.

Ramón answered direct questions only, yes to this, no to that, up to the point the cop asked him how long he'd been in Westin. "Until today," he said.

I helped him pull his sleeping bag and some clothes out of the wreckage of Sonny's camper. As we were loading them into his Thunderbird, Reno came over to us, waving our pay envelopes. Both of us took them, folded them into our pockets. When Reno figured out that Ramón was quitting, he said, "There's gonna *be* work. Number sixteen gonna need crew, and you're about the best man we got...." Ramón smiled. Reno smiled back, as if they'd been on the same team before, as if they'd both seen it bad, ironic, stupid before, but never this bad, ironic, stupid. "Well then, where the hell you going?" Reno said, as if he might just pack his things and come along.

"Rangely," said Ramón.

"Shit," said Reno. "I'm damned if I'll go down there and pull rods on those old wells. That's janitor's work."

Ramón smiled, then laughed, then Reno laughed. "If you do find something down there, would you call me, if I give you my number?" Ramón nodded, a nod that meant I like you, too, but there won't be any call. Then the two of them shook hands and looked each other in the eyes in a way that men usually save for good-bye.

Reno and BJ helped me peel the Maverick out from under the chain link that the dozer had folded onto the hood as it crushed the fence. While we were at it, Sonny limped over. "You might want to leave your car where it is till the insurance man comes in," he said. "Get it all fixed up on the company's tab." He tapped his temple, meaning, If you're smart.

I told him I was going back to the trailer to get some sleep before I fell down. "Probably a good idea," he said. "Might need you tonight. You and Reno and the Mex and BJ, for evening tour on sixteen."

I shook my head. "I have plans."

"What plans?"

I was about to tell him it was none of his goddamn business when Reno said, "Ramón's twisted off. I gave him his check, and he's gone."

"What do you mean, gone? I need him. You better just go after his ass right now."

"In what?" said Reno.

By the time I parked the Maverick in the midafternoon quiet of our unnamed street in Yellow Creek Estates I was tired enough that I thought of saving myself the last few steps to the trailer, forgetting the shower, forgetting the bed, just cranking the seat back and sleeping right there, with the sun through the windshield on my lap, a perfect breeze on my face. I changed my mind when I pictured Monday pulling up in her truck, finding me behind the wheel in a filthy, sweating, snoring, drooling heap. Not that she hadn't probably found her dates like that before. Maybe she even liked men who smelled of mud and grease, or else what was she doing in an oil field?

There was a note on the screen door. *I'm cooking*, it said in a large, smooth grade-school hand. *Seven o'clock. Tails optional. Monday.* Below the words she'd drawn a map with an arrowed line that began at our trailer, then snaked its way through the entire park, in and out of the cul-de-sacs, then around the perimeter until it arrived across the street at her trailer.

I don't remember showering, but I must have, because I was clean and had on clean jockey shorts when I woke to the slamming of truck doors. It was a little after six. I looked out my window and saw the brothers leaving a rented truck at the curb. Each of them was carrying his own six-pack of tall boys, and they were arguing. Bub was saying no way he was going back out on number 16 tonight with a crew full of worms, not if Sonny was staying in town to get drunk or chase waitresses or whatever the hell he had in mind. I closed the bedroom door just before the two of them stepped into the trailer. Then I got out my notebook.

"You'll do it, all right," said Sonny. "Or I'll run your ass out of here, just like any other fool don't do what I need him to do."

There was a silence. Beers popped.

"Call me fool..." said Bub. "You *think* I am, don't you? Else you never would have fucked my wife and thought you could get away with it."

"I never fucked her," said Sonny in a tone that didn't protest quite enough. "Where'd you get that?"

"She told me you did, Sonny boy. While I was in jail that week after New Year. Said you came sniffing around like a dog...."

"She fucked a lot of guys," said Sonny. "Everybody." He was yelling. "She fucked everybody...."

Something broke a window, probably a full beer, I thought.

"You gonna pull your little knife?" said Bub, then the weight of what must have been both of them slammed the wall hard enough that I almost came off the bed, and for a full minute after that the trailer rocked and thumped as if it were being towed too fast over bad road. There was a pause in which I could hear both of them heaving for air, then a strange squeal, then the sound of the couch or an end table snapping, a lamp, something glass shattering.

Payday, I wrote in large block letters. *Sitting here listening to a couple of big, dumb rednecks settling their accounts in the only way...*

That turned out to be the last sentence I was going to write in that notebook, and when Sonny came crashing through the bedroom door, it felt as if it might be the last sentence I was ever going to write in any notebook. He hit it as if he'd been thrown by four men, blew the lock, blew the top hinge, landed on me where I sat, and the two of us rode his momentum off the bed, onto the floor. I heard Bub follow him in, but I couldn't see anything. Sonny was on top of me, sweating, bleeding, trying to get his wind.

"Come on... you little peckerface," said Bub between his own heavy breaths, "get some more."

Sonny didn't answer. He rolled himself off me and sat against the wall. When I sat, I saw Bub catch sight of the open notebook in the middle of the bed. He picked it up.

I pulled myself off the floor and stood there in the corner of my little room, in my jockey shorts, hoping maybe he couldn't read my handwriting, or that maybe he couldn't read at all.

"Shit," he said, and turned a page. "Shit. This little cocksucker's got everything wrote down, every damn word we said."

Sonny sat there looking at his brother as if he didn't get it.

Bub flipped backward through the pages. "Shit," he kept saying. "He's some kind of newspaperman, or..." Something he read stopped him. I don't know what it was. Something I never would have said to his face, I was sure of that; certainly not while I stood there in my shorts, in a small corner of a small room with him between me and the door.

I felt tears in my throat and thought of begging, and I might have if he hadn't filled his big dirty fist with pages, torn them out, then thrown them at my face, which turned out to be the blessed moment at which fear and anger mix and things begin to take care of themselves. I lunged across the bed for the notebook, missed, and he hit me square in the face with it. Then he used my hair to roll me over and hit me again, this time with the spine of the book, under my right eye. I kicked for his balls and came close enough that he let go of my hair, which gave me room to get up and get kicked in the thigh, then punched in the nose, hard. Then all I saw was rug.

I heard Sonny yell, "Leave him be, goddamnit," but Bub had me by the hair again. He was on his knees, next to me, and this time when he levered my head around, he showed me a handful of torn and crumpled pages and said, "You're gonna eat this shit, every fucking word." Then he pushed it at my mouth, gouged it around trying to get it in. All I could taste was blood.

Sonny pulled him off from behind and was swearing down at his brother when Bub grabbed his legs out from under him. Then the two of them were at it again.

I crawled out of the bedroom and used the knob on the front door to pull myself to my feet. My nose was bleeding all over me. I thought of getting a towel out of the bathroom, then heard Sonny yelp and decided to get out of the trailer, try for the Maverick.

There were half a dozen people on the sidewalk, including a couple of children whose mothers grabbed them as I came down the drive. I had my nose pinched with both hands, and couldn't make out faces in the group, but I heard somebody say it looked like I'd been shot in the face, somebody else that they ought to call an ambulance. I started to say, I'm all right, but nothing came out. Then, as I got the car door open, I felt a hand on my shoulder. It was Monday. "Sweet Jesus," she said when I looked at her. "Come with me." I picked my jacket off the front seat, covered my face with it, then she led me gently across the street saying, "Watch the curb...watch the steps..." into her trailer.

I sat, then lay, on a cold plastic couch, which reminded me I was almost naked, and in that moment, that absurd moment, with one eye swollen shut, my nose dead numb, my ribs being danced around by an almost electrical sort of pain, and the rest of me splattered with blood, I heard Monday rustling around, running water, and all I could think of was her hands on me, my hands on her, and I got a hard-on.

I don't know how long one of those things lasts after you lose consciousness. It was gone when I came to, about five minutes later, Monday said, although she didn't mention anything about the knob she'd had to work around as she wiped me down with a wet towel, packed my nose with tissue, put a pillow under my head, covered me with a blanket, set a cold lamb chop on my left eye.

"That was dinner," she said when I reached for it. "But you don't look that hungry right now. Leave it there. It works. I used to think it was a joke till I got jacked in the eye in Gillette. It keeps the swelling way down. I used beef, but I don't know why lamb wouldn't work just as good." She was standing over me in tight black jeans and a pink satin shirt with arrows at the pockets. The dinette table behind her was set for two, a bunch of yellow mums at the middle. "What happened?"

"They found the notebook."

She shook her head. "Everybody's a critic," she said. "Do you want to go to the hospital?"

"I'll be all right."

"Your nose is pointing to the left," she said.

"I'm just glad it's still there," I said. "I can't feel it."

"You will," she said. "Wait a minute." She came back with a glass of water and a small pill. "Percodan," she said. "You better take it. Turns everything into a faint little echo."

I tried to sit. My ribs screamed; I moaned.

She sat on the edge of the couch. "Just hold the lamb chop," she said, then put the pill on my tongue, tilted my head forward with one hand, tipped the glass to my lips with the other. The water mixed with the blood that was still dripping into my throat and made a taste that reminded me of the metallic dust that hung in the air around the yard.

"Sorry about dinner," I said.

"Me, too. Seems like every time I cook for a guy, something happens to him. Usually a quart of whiskey, something like that." She smiled, combed the hair off my forehead with her fingers in a way that made me think she might have kissed me if it hadn't been for the lamb chop on my eye. "I don't do it much anymore."

"What about Jesse?"

"He didn't eat that much. He was on the white-powder diet."

"Is he coming back?"

"I don't know. The police are looking for him, but the rent's paid up on this trailer to the end of next month. I expect he'll creep back sometime before that to collect his things."

"Including you?"

"Not including me," she said in a way that was irritated at how I'd put the question. She got up and walked to the front window. "The cops are across the street. You want to talk to them?" I told her no. "I know the one with all the muscles. He busted Jesse."

"What for?"

"What do you think?"

"Dealing?"

She nodded, still looking out the window. "Not a bad guy for a cop," she said. "He came back after Jesse jumped bail, asked a few questions. Made a pass at me. Kinda sweet. I thought about it." She stood there, a silhouette against the twilight in the window, all dressed up, as lonely as the flowers on the table.

I sat up. "What are you doing?" she said.

"It's all right," I told her. "That pill's making a difference. I feel better, a lot better."

"Strong stuff," she said. "You *feel* better, but you're not, so just stay where you are."

"I'm good, I feel *good*," I said.

"Hasn't done anything for the way you look," she said. "You're just high. Relax."

I stood. My head spun, then settled. "I'm fine," I said. "Let's have dinner." I handed her the lamb chop.

"You're gonna fall down," she said.

"Come on," I said. "The table's all set, smells like potatoes in the oven. Let's just go ahead and eat before this thing wears off."

"All right," she said, holding up the chop. "This one's yours. And if you want to dress, there are two suitcases in the closet in the big bedroom. I mean, you don't have to dress if you don't want to..." She paused, looked at my blood-spattered shorts. "Yes you do," she said. "Back bedroom."

I stopped in the bathroom on my way, got the Kleenex out of my nose, and splashed my face with cold water before I looked at myself in the mirror. Could have been worse, I thought. The eye was ugly, but not as fat or purple as it felt. The nose wandered left, but only a little, and by the tender mercies of the Percodan none of me, not even the ribs, felt what had really happened.

The zippered suitcases were side by side in a closet of their own, below a dozen shirts that had been laundered, and hangered, and arranged above the bags in a way that seemed to say, Here's your luggage, what's your hurry? I found a pair of yellow sweat-pants among the neatly folded socks and shorts and jeans in the first bag. I matched them to the only shirt in the closet that wasn't black or white: a red Hawaiian job painted with orchids and volcanoes.

"Going to the beach?" Monday said as I sat at the little table. She was at the sink washing lettuce.

"Only thing I could find that didn't make me look like a gunfighter," I said.

"I bought that shirt for him. He never wore it."

I didn't say anything. I was thinking of the red merry widow I'd bought for Suzanne that she'd never worn, remembering the low blush on her face when she'd opened the box, the melancholy smile that said, This is not me, this is not us.

"I made him try it on. He said it made him look like a lawn flamingo. Which it did, actually."

"You have a picture of him?"

"There were only two or three," she said. "He took them. Said he didn't want to see them on a post-office wall. Delusions of grandeur. Armed and dangerous. Wanted dead or alive. I think his mother saw too many gangster movies when she was pregnant."

She set a salad on the table. I pictured her in the red merry widow.

"What are you going to do when the rent runs out?" I said.

"Oh . . ." she said. "California, I guess. I thought about it when Jesse left, but I didn't want to go back broke. I have a little money now."

"I'll find something," she said when I asked her what she'd do in California. "One thing I learned in Wyoming is how to work. Actually, I learned a lot of things in Wyoming, but how to work is probably the best of them. Growing up at the beach, all I learned was how to play, which isn't a bad thing, but, you know, you turn twenty-five at the beach, see all the pretty little sixteen-year-olds running around doing *exactly* what you did, and you start to feel like the playground supervisor." She pulled a casserole of scalloped potatoes out of the oven, slid the chops under the broiler. "When are you leaving? You are leaving, aren't you?"

"Not for a while," I said.

"Great," she said. "What are you going to do? Move back in with your good pal across the street?"

"I know a rooming house in town. It's a shithole, but it'll do. I may just get my stuff and move in there."

"And do what for work?" she said. "I mean, in case you haven't looked at your face, I'd say the guy across the street just gave you notice."

"Hell," I said. "I was through with that outfit before brother Bub got loose on me. This is nothing. What you're looking at here is light work up against what happened last night out in the hills. On a rig, the first working rig I'd ever been near, something snapped, I don't know what, and some kind of godawful metal rod tore loose and hit one of the guys in the chest. Hard. He was standing right next to me, then all of a sudden he was lying in the mud looking up..." I saw Marlin's eyes again, and for a moment I lost my place in the story.

"Is he all right?" said Monday.

"I don't know. He could be dead. Nobody cares. All anybody cared was whether the fucking rig was all right. No. That's not exactly true. His crew chief cared. Came onto the yard this morning like some avenging angel on a bulldozer. Tore up everything that had a D and J sticker on it. It was beautiful...." The painkiller gained another notch on me. I leaned back in my chair and sighed.

"I think we better skip dinner," said Monday. "You need to lie down."

"Not yet," I said. "I'm all right. The best I've been since I arrived, in a way. Ever since I got here, I've felt like someone was pointing a gun at me. Now they've pulled the trigger, and this is all I got. Flesh wounds. Don't get me wrong, it's enough. Whatever illusions I had about hard work, I'm cured. I'm bad at it, and it scares the shit out of me. And I've definitely learned whatever the Neanderthal brothers had to teach me, but..." I stopped and heard how stupid what I was about to say was going to sound when I put it into words.

"But what?" Monday said.

"The worse things get, the better the story," I said.

She rolled her eyes, shook her head.

"Something to tell the grandchildren," I said. "Just what you said you were looking for.... Go somewhere you don't belong, somewhere dangerous, get in over your head, get scared, maybe get hurt. Tried and true."

"Too bad they didn't shoot you," she said.

"Sick, huh?" I said.

"Maybe you ought to try a love story next time," she said.

"I'm not up for anything *that* dangerous," I said.

A half-smile came onto her face. "Well," she said without looking at me, "you got your story...your beating... now you can leave, right?"

"It's not finished," I said. "Loose ends." Now she looked at me. "I have to find out if Marlin's all right... what's going to happen to Sonny...the guy on the bulldozer...and..." I stopped short of putting her name in the sentence, but the way I was looking at her, she heard it anyway.

She got up and went to the stove to turn the chops. "What about your wife?" she said over her shoulder.

"The last time I talked to her, she said she wanted a divorce."

"When was that?"

"A week ago, something like that."

"Did you try to talk her out of it?"

"No," I said.

"Maybe you ought to call her back," she said. "These things are never over the first time they're over. People change their minds."

I wondered if she was trying to tell me something about her and Jesse. Not the way those suitcases were packed, I decided.

"I have some wine," she said. "I'm not sure how it will go with Percodan...." She put the bottle on the table with a corkscrew. I opened it, poured a sip, tried it.

"Ah yes," I said as she set our dinner on the table. "A stoop-shouldered little wine, perfect for those occasions when everything tastes a little like blood anyway...." I stopped. She wasn't even smiling. "Monday," I said.

"Thanks. This is very sweet. You're very sweet." I stood, leaned across the table, kissed her on the cheek. Still no smile. "What is it?" I asked her.

"You should call your wife," she said.

"I will," I said, then sat there eating my lamb chop, feeling as if she'd just told me to go home.

Then she said, "You can use my phone."

We ate without talking. The food looked good, but I couldn't smell it or taste it and I wasn't hungry anyway. I tried to imagine what was going on behind Monday's melancholy eyes, tried to think of a question that would invite her to say some of it, but I couldn't. I wanted to tell her that Suzanne and I were finished, that it was a mercy, that for a year, maybe more, the two of us had quietly punished each other not by what we said or did, but simply by being ourselves. I didn't get a chance to say any of it. The wine caught up with the pill, the mums blurred, and I started to have trouble with my utensils. When I dropped the fork and was unable to pick it up in two tries, Monday took me by the arm, walked me down the hall, and sat me on the edge of her bed.

"I'm going to put another pill on the night table," she said. "You're going to need it when you wake up."

"Where are you sleeping?" I said as she laid me back, covered me.

"In one of the other bedrooms," she said.

"I can't take your bed. I'll sleep in the other..."

"Stay where you are," she said from the bathroom.

"Then you stay here, too," I said, as she put the pill and a glass of water on the night table. "It's a big bed."

"It's not that big," she said.

"Come on," I said. "I'm not in any shape to..."

She laughed, then said, "Are you kidding? Do you know you had a hard-on when I found you passed out on the couch?" Then she kissed my smile and turned out the light in what seemed like one move.

I woke in darkness, to pain that had stolen out from under the Percodan and gathered into a rage while I slept. My head was a ball of pain, my torso a barrel of it. My nose felt as if it had been nailed to my face. I yelped when I tried to sit, then moaned when I rolled toward the nightstand to grope for the pill.

I felt the trailer move slightly, heard footsteps on the carpet, saw a light come on in the hallway. "Don't move," said Monday as her silhouette came through the door. She sat on the edge of the bed and reached for the water and the pill. She was in a T-shirt. Her legs were bare. She put the pill on my tongue, lifted my head gently, put the glass to my lips. "It'll take a few minutes," she said. "Lie quiet."

"Sorry...wake you up," I said.

"I wasn't asleep."

"I took your bed...."

"It's not that," she said.

"How long have I been out?"

"Two hours, I don't know, maybe three. Don't talk." She made a weak smile. I closed my eyes, felt the beginnings of the drug fog trying to take the detail out of my agonies.

"Don't go," I said as she stood, and whether it was the pill or the sight of her standing there, the pain lost the worst of its grip and I sat up. "Please."

"I don't want you to think..." she said as if she were trying to get it right and it was going to be difficult, "that I don't want to sleep with you. I do...but...I don't want to wreck a friendship if that's what we have here...and if it's going to be more than a friendship...I'm not sure this is a good time to start it...with me just out of a stupid romance...and you...married...and probably going back to your wife...." She stopped, shook her head slowly. "And if it's not friendship, and not a romance...I just don't need a piece of ass."

"I don't, either," I said. Then, "That's a lie. But never mind. You're right. The timing stinks." She bent to pull the covers up. I kissed her cheek, tasted a tear. Then felt her hands in my hair, her knee on the mattress beside me, her lips nipping gently at my swollen eye, at my mouth. I lay there feeling no turn to yes, trying to guess why, how?

"Porcupine love," she said as she undid the buttons on my shirt. "I don't want to hurt you."

"Can't be helped," I said. And then it was like being cradled and beaten at the same time, a confusion of ecstasy and pain so pretty that it would have been all right, that night, to die of it.

There was midmorning sunlight on the sheets next to me when I opened my eyes. Monday was gone. I lay still, feeling every broken part of myself, wondering why the body forgets pleasure overnight but stores pain no matter what.

Things felt a little better when I finally got myself up, got moving. The ribs were the worst of it, but even they were all right as long as I walked like a zombie. My head ached, my nose stung, and the eye was uglier than the night before when I got a look at it in the bathroom mirror. I filled the sink with cold water, floated my face in it.

There was a note on the kitchen table next to the flowers. *Back in a while*, it said. *Don't go anywhere*. Below that was a list headed *Things to do: #1. Eat something. #2. Take this*. The *i* in the word *this* was dotted with a Percodan. *#3. Call your wife.*

I put the pill in my pocket. I still had to retrieve my

things from the trailer across the street, and I didn't want
to be rummy if the brothers were there, if, by some chance,
they hadn't killed each other. I looked out the front window. The rented pickup was gone. The Maverick sat where
I'd left it.

I got orange juice out of the refrigerator, sat at the
kitchen table, looked at the phone on the wall. *#3. Call
your wife.* And say what? Burn the greenhouse and store
my things, I don't know when I'm coming back? Send the
divorce papers general delivery? Her name is Monday,
what's his? Oh hell, I told myself. It doesn't matter what
you say, and you'll know how to say it when you hear her
voice.

I phoned her at work. The receptionist said she wasn't
there. I asked if she was home for the day. "Who's calling?"
she said, and when I told her, she got the tone in her voice
that's afraid of saying the wrong thing. "Oh," she said.
"I'm not sure ... I ... just a minute." It irritated me to think
that Suzanne was ducking the call, and I expected her to
come on the line saying she was busy, couldn't we talk some
other time? No, we can't, I thought while I waited. We'll
talk now, end it now, one clean stroke, no mess, no guilt,
no villains.

But it was her friend Tracy who came on the line.
There was an officious sort of anger in her voice. "Suzanne's not here." I asked where she was. "I don't think I
can tell you that," she said. "She doesn't want to talk to
you."

"Wait a minute," I said, and thought, You scheming,
cheating bitch ... "*You* don't tell me that," I said. "*She* tells
me that. Where the hell is she?"

There was a silence long enough that I thought she
might hang up. "With David," she said.

"David?" He wasn't even on the list I'd made. "Who
the fuck is David ... and what the fuck's going on?"

"You don't know?"

"I'm in the middle of a goddamn oil field," I said. "I don't know anything."

There was another pause, then, "Suzanne was arrested yesterday," she said. "For growing marijuana."

8

Monday pulled in behind the Maverick as I humped my duffel bag into the trunk. She came out of her little truck smiling.

"You're not moving into that room you told me about, are you? Why don't you just move that stuff across the street. I mean for as long as you stay. No strings, don't worry."

I walked back up the driveway and into the trailer without saying anything. "Wait a minute," she said. "What's wrong?" Then, as she followed me into the wreckage of the living room, "Whoa ... there goes the damage deposit."

"Monday ..." I said, and before I could finish the sentence, she read through the pause and finished it for me.

"You called California," she said. I nodded. "You're leaving now."

"I don't want to," I told her.

"Spare me," she said, and turned to stare out the broken window. "I promised myself I wasn't going to be surprised by this, damnit."

"Listen," I said. "Suzanne was arrested yesterday for a greenhouse full of weed that belonged to me."

"What?" she said.

"My bust," I said. "She doesn't even garden, for chrissakes."

"Is she in jail?"

"Her boyfriend bailed her out," I said. "David. Whoever the fuck he is."

I knelt to roll my sleeping bag.

"How many plants were there?"

"About a dozen," I said. "Probably half-dead. She didn't want anything to do with it. I left it there like a goddamn time bomb. She didn't deserve this."

"They're not going to..." She stopped. I looked at her. "I mean, twelve plants, Marin County...if her lawyer's any good, she'll get off even if you don't go back."

"Oh yeah, perfect," I said. "She pays the fine, goes on probation, and I become a fugitive. Perfect, except I don't think I have enough black shirts for the work."

It was a nasty thing to say, and for a second something happened on her face that made me think she might cry. I stood, moved to hug her. She let me: hands at her sides, body stiff with the effort it was taking to hold herself together. "I'm sorry," I said.

I let her go, she pulled away, then manufactured a smile that wasn't a smile, and said, "Do you have everything?"

"I can't find the notebook," I said. "Bastards must have taken it. I've searched."

"In the garbage?"

"First place I looked."

"Let me try," she said, and headed for Sonny's room. "There's nothing I don't know about these trailers."

I carried the rest of my gear to the Maverick, threw it in the backseat, then got behind the wheel and waited.

Ten minutes later, she came down the driveway empty-handed.

"It's gone," she said when she got to the car. "I'm going to look again, but..."

"Never mind," I said.

"Can you remember what's in it?"

"It doesn't matter," I said.

"It does matter," she said, angry. Her eyes filled with tears. "This can't be for nothing, you didn't come here for nothing, you can't go away with nothing." Her tears weren't for the notebook.

"Monday," I said. "I'll be back...."

"Don't say that." She wiped at her eyes. "Just don't say that. Just don't lie to me. I don't need it. I feel stupid enough already...for thinking..." She shook her head, collected herself.

"I don't know how long..." She put a palm up, meaning, Don't say it. She turned, walked a few steps, then ran the rest of the way to her trailer.

I saw Suzanne for the first time a few days after I got back, in the courthouse, with her lawyer. David. I recognized him as the ambitious young suit and tie who did the legal work for Suzanne's company. We'd met once at a fund-raising dinner a few months before I'd left for Wyoming. When Suzanne introduced us, he shook my hand, looked at her, then back at me, and said, "Some guys have all the luck." It was a moment that might have put him near the top of my notebook list of Suzanne's possible boyfriends if I'd remembered it, if there'd been anything otherwise memorable about him.

That afternoon in the long hallway outside the hearing room, he stood with his arm around her shoulder, his mouth almost touching her ear, speaking softly. I was almost to them before Suzanne recognized my beardless, freshly beaten face. David stiffened when she said my name.

"My God, what did they do to you?" she said. She looked tired, full of tranquilizers, maybe.

"Looks worse than it is," I told her. Then I kissed her on the temple and said, "I'm sorry."

When she tried to say something but couldn't, David tightened the grip around her shoulder and said, "This is awkward, I know, but..."

I almost asked him, "What's awkward?" to make him say it: "Suzanne and I are lovers." But there was something sincere and unlawyerly in his face, something just apologetic enough to make me want to spare all of us the cheap shots and pissy monologues that had played in my head on the long drive from Wyoming to Marin.

I liked him even better in the hearing room, the way he stood up next to Suzanne as if he'd left a big white horse somewhere in the parking lot. The county attorney said he had no objections to the motion that all charges against Suzanne be dropped. He offered the judge my sworn statement that the crop was mine, and that Suzanne had never used or cultivated marijuana, then referred him to one of the two exhibits on the evidence table: the instruction sheet I had left tacked to the inside of the greenhouse door.

The judge asked me if I'd written it. I told him yes. "What's this quote at the top," he said. "'...seeds and plants, and what will thrive and rise, and what the genius of the soil denies.'"

"Virgil," I told him. "From a long poem about gardening. He grew up on a farm."

"He ever grow any pot?" said the judge. There was chuckling from the clerk and the county attorney.

"If he did, he left it out of the poem," I said.

"All right," said the judge. "Charges against your client are dismissed, Mr. Hale." David thanked him, hugged Suzanne.

"How much do we have here?" asked the judge, pointing at Exhibit A, a garbage bag with the plants in it. Two kilograms, the county attorney told him.

"You have a lawyer?" said the judge, and when I shook my head, "Well, you're going to need one before you plead."

I looked at David. He looked at Suzanne, then said, "I'll represent the defendant, Your Honor."

"Fine," said the judge. "You want to confer?"

"We don't have to do that," I said. "I plead guilty."

"Plea is entered," said the judge. "Defendant released on his own recognizance. Sentencing in two weeks."

I spent the next ten days alone, in my chair, at my typewriter, trying to reconstruct the notebook, but all it did was depress me. Especially the entries with Monday in them. I resisted calling her for as long as I could, and when I finally picked up the phone to do it, my line was dead. I hadn't looked at the mail since I'd been back, and when did, there was a pink notice from the phone company, then a red one with instructions on how to have the service reconnected. There were other overdue bills, and as I opened them, it became clear from the dates that Suzanne hadn't lived in the house, or even visited, in a long time.

Near the bottom of the stack was a letter from my editor friend. On the envelope was the logo of an outdoor magazine called *Compass*. The postmark was Chicago.

. . . if you're still alive, it said, *. . . if you still have fingers enough to use a computer keyboard, and if you are over the delusion that grunt work is good for the soul, why don't you come to Chicago. I need someone to edit the piton and yak butter sections of this*

magazine, do a little writing. Paycheck every two weeks, view of
Lake Michigan, new chairs...

The morning of the sentence hearing, I met David in
his office. Suzanne was there. She looked better, and this
time she kissed me, said *she* was sorry. David-the-boyfriend
watched us, awkward again in his role as agent and ben-
eficiary of the end of Suzanne and me. When he saw the
tears start into her eyes, and into mine, he said, "Well..."
then sat into his chair and became the lawyer.

"I've talked to the county attorney," he said, "And I
don't think anybody wants you to go to jail on this. You
don't have any record, and I think the judge liked you...
that Virgil stuff. With luck I think we're talking probation
and a fine. You have any money?"

"About two grand," I said, and thought, Bless your
thieving ass, Sonny. My check, when I'd opened it, was for
$2,004. He hadn't deducted the rent, or the advances, he'd
added time and bumped my base rate to $10.50 an hour.

"That may be enough," he said. "Cross your fingers."
He reached for a manila folder at the side of his desk.
"There is one other thing," he said. "I don't know that this
is the moment, but I'm not sure that there will be a better
one..." He handed me a sheaf of papers. "This is the
divorce agreement Suzanne asked me to draw up. It's very
straightforward, what's hers is hers, what's yours is yours,
just as you came into the marriage. But you probably ought
to read it over, take it to another lawyer, have him..."

I signed it while he talked.

"You ought to read it, at least," he said.

"You want me to check it for spelling, or what?" I said.

"As an attorney, I have to..."

"Save it up for the sentencing," I said.

And he did. When the time came, he spoke with gusto

of my long and distinguished efforts in a difficult profession, then noted that my return from the oil fields to face charges was testimony to the fact that I was not only a thoughtful and literate man, a man who read Virgil and Shakespeare, but an honorable one as well, a responsible one...and on and on until he made it sound a shame that men like me didn't run for public office. He ended the toast by saying that I had been offered a top job on a national magazine based in Chicago and that he hoped whatever the sentence, it would allow me to pursue the success that waited for me there.

When David sat, the judge asked me if I had anything to say. About myself, or that guy he just described? I thought, but I didn't say it. I shook my head no.

"All right," said the judge. "Don't do it again. The fine is fifteen hundred dollars."

The day before I left, Suzanne found me turning the dirt in the greenhouse, erasing the ragged holes the sheriff's men had left in the wake of the early harvest.

"Planting something?" she said. She was alone. She looked great.

"Just getting the soil ready," I said. "For the next tenant...whoever."

"I only came by to get a few last things."

"I put them in a couple of carton boxes. In the bedroom."

"I saw," she said. "It was sweet of you." She smiled, looked at me in a way that made me wish I hadn't sold the bed. I heard her thinking the same thing, then felt her let go of the thought. "Looks like you got the car all ready."

"Oh yeah," I said. "If duct tape were chrome, it's a pimpmobile. I'm not sure it'll make it all the way to Chicago, but what the hell. If it dies somewhere out there on old 80, I'll bury it with honors."

"You driving straight through?"

"I'll stop in Wyoming," I said. "See who I can find. I'm not sure who'll still be there, because from what I read in the papers, the boom is dying fast. But I left in a hurry, left some unfinished business."

"A woman?" she said.

"Not really," I said. "Maybe." Then, "Yes. But it's a little sketchy. Nuts, actually."

"If it weren't nuts, you wouldn't have anything to do with it," she said. "We were nuts." I smiled, nodded, and when it felt like tears again, I stuck the shovel in the dirt, got my arms around her, and the two of us stood in the pretty light of the empty hothouse just long enough to say good-bye without having to use the words.

One of the sentinel rigs that stood along old 80 on the outskirts of Westin was gone the morning I rolled back into town. The other was still there, but without crew, without the American flag in the crown.

I pulled onto the shoulder and stopped across from D and J. Three oil barrels and a small heap of scrap sat near the middle of the yard. Otherwise, it belonged to the prairie dogs again. Empty dirt. A For Lease sign hung on the chain link facing the highway.

I took the off-ramp onto Yellow Creek Road wondering if the dying Maverick was up to the drubbing that began where the pavement ran out. I slowed for the cattle guard that had been the last of the hardtop, then rolled onto a beautifully smooth two-lane ribbon of asphalt so new it still shined. It took me ten minutes to make the drive that had taken half an hour only four weeks before. The one truck that passed me headed for the highway was pulling a trailer like the one Sonny and I had shared. The old man behind the wheel waved as he went by; and as I came around the hillside that let onto the first view of the park, it became clear that they had finished the road just in time for the exodus: Blank dirt rectangles were scattered among the trailers that were left as if some hungry thing had found its way under the fence.

Inside the park brand-new street signs sat on every corner. I followed Eagle Road to Owl, took Owl to Rabbit, then turned left onto the street Sonny and I had shared: Coyote. Close enough, I thought: Nobody was going to name a street Snake.

A black pickup with every chrome touch in the catalog was parked at the curb in front of Monday's, and when I saw it, all I could think was, Fool . . . you should have called, should have known. Her truck sat in the driveway, a bicycle and a large suitcase roped to the roof rack. I passed the trailer, without slowing, without looking, then looped through the cul-de-sac and doubled back. This time as I passed, the front door opened, and Monday jumped the steps to the ground, ran barefoot into the street, smiling, buttoning her jeans, yelling, "I don't believe it."

I stopped in the middle of the street. She got her hands on my head through the window, kissed me, then said it again. "I don't believe it's you."

"Sometimes," I said, "for reasons nobody understands, things go right."

"But what are you doing here?"

"On my way to Chicago." She looked at me as if I'd said Katmandu. "Got a job."

"Great," she said.

"Better than jail . . . I think." She laughed. "I missed you," I told her.

"Yes," she said. "I know. I told myself I was going to look for you in California. I just didn't know. . . ."

"You leaving?"

"Today," she said. "I didn't want to be the last one out of town."

Come with me, I almost said, but stopped when I spotted a tall, dark figure behind the screen door. He was naked. When she saw me staring, Monday looked over her shoulder. "Jesse," she said.

"I saw the truck."

"He came by for his things," she said. "I told you he would...."

"Looks like he stayed the night," I said, and whatever she heard in my voice changed her face. She took her hands off the car door.

"What the hell," I said. "People change their minds."

"Please," she said. "Don't do this. It was good-bye. That's all. These things aren't that simple. What about you and your wife?"

"We *hugged* good-bye," I said.

"And what the hell difference does it make?" she said, all the way angry now. "Good-bye is good-bye...if you could just get your goddamn male ego out of the way for two minutes."

"I can do that," I said, and pulled the gearshift into "drive."

"Wait," she said as I drove off. "Please...I have something for you."

It was all wrong anyway, I told myself on the way back over the new road toward 80. And aren't you glad you stopped to make sure, to piss on this good woman for no good reason, to let your cowardly heart disguise another cowardly moment as something other than fear.

I drove into town for a drink. Maybe ten, maybe a room for the night, at the Mesa, which, said the big sign, had vacancies these days.

A single lonely figure sat over a tall beer at the far end of the bar. I put as many stools between us as I could so that I wouldn't have to hear what had driven him to beer at eleven in the morning. There was no bartender.

"He's stepped out, I don't know where to," said a familiar voice across the long empty space between us.

"Sonny," I said.

He turtled his head, squinted. "Well I'll be fucked and fucked again," he said, getting off his stool. "I thought you was long gone."

"I was," I said, as he shook my hand. "Just stopping through. What are you doing here? Looked to me like D and J was out of business."

"They is," he said. "Along with half the outfits in town."

"Happened fast."

"It'll do that," he said. "Prices start to fall, the big companies pull off this deep oil like it wasn't never there." A kid in a janitor's jumpsuit came through the stockroom door carrying a case of beer. "We're gonna need a couple of those down here," said Sonny.

"What'd you do, hire on with somebody else?" I said.

"Nope. I got lucky. After D and J run everybody off, they asked me to stick around sell off the equipment. On commission." He winked. "Done pretty good, too. Real good. Better than I done in six months working for wages. Get enough to buy into a muffler shop down home. Old boy down the bank couldn't believe it when I sold both those Coopers in one month. Told me, 'We got a good news–bad news joke around here these days. Good news is we's offering a toaster or a oil rig to anybody opens a checking account. Bad news is we outta toasters.'"

"Maybe you found your hidden talent," I said.

"Shit . . ." he said, then looked at me sideways the way he had the night he'd hired me. "Talk about hidden talents . . . I knew you wasn't no teacher. I didn't know what you *was* exactly, but I'll tell you what. Nobody read writing like yours on a blackboard. I know that." He looked at his beer. "You could have told me you was a writer."

"Oh, come on," I said. "You never would have hired me if you'd known I was taking notes."

"Maybe not," he said. "But you could have interviewed me, I could have told you some things...."

"Not the same as taking the beating for yourself," I said.

"Well, if it's a beating you were looking for...you got a good one from 'ole Bub, didn't you."

"Still hurts," I said.

"He wasn't finished, neither. He read some of that stuff you'd wrote about him, wanted to go across the street and tear your balls off...if the cops hadn't come."

"Where is he now?" I said.

"He's getting some cigarettes. He'll be right back." He watched my face change, probably saw the hair stand up on the back of my neck, then laughed. "Shit," he said. "I run him off the day after he cut loose like that. I think he's back down in Texas, in jail is what my wife said, which is probably where he belongs."

"What about Marlin?" I said.

"Marlin?"

"The kid who got hurt out on number sixteen."

"Shit, that's right, you wouldn't have heard about that," he said. "Papers around here made a big deal out of it. His rig injury wasn't that bad is what the doctors said. He was going to live through that...'cept they put him on a plane and crashed it halfway to Salt Lake. Killed everybody. Ain't that a thing?"

I sat there trying to believe it, wanting to see the newspaper, feeling my stomach move.

"Old Tom's in a booby hatch they got for veterans someplace, I don't know where." He looked straight at me. "You gonna write a book about all this, or what?"

"I don't know," I said. "It's all a little blurry right now. I just...I don't know."

"You got it all down in that book of yours, it looked like to me. So's all you'd have to do is just..."

"The notebook's gone," I said. "I figured you and Bub probably..."

"The hell it's gone," he said. "Your girlfriend has it."

"What?" I said.

"That's right. Pretty little one across the street. She walked in right in the middle of me running Bub out of there, said if we didn't give it to her, then she was gonna go through every damn thing we owned till she found it, and I mean, she had knives in her eyes. I didn't see nothing else to do but give it to her, the way she was standing there. Bub didn't say nothing, either. I think he was worse surprised than me. Anyways, I got it outta my truck and gave it over. She said she was gonna carry it out to you in Frisco."

"Damn..." was all I could say out of the storm of things I was thinking.

"I don't know what you two had going," said Sonny, "but that girl's in *love*. If I was you..."

"Sonny," I said. "I have to go. I just did something so mean and stupid... I can't even talk about it. But you were great to me, I mean it. I won't forget it." I put a twenty on the bar, shook his hand.

"All right," he said as I backed toward the stairs. "But do me a favor. If you do write a book, I'd appreciate it if you wouldn't play up my drinking."

Something under the hood of the Maverick moaned when I turned the key. I moaned with it, then swore, then begged out loud to the rhythm of the tired grinding, "Please, please, please... baby, please," and it caught. I laid a beautiful cloud of almost pure white smoke over the parking lot on my way out.

I was in the viaduct under 80 headed for Yellow Creek Road when I saw Monday's truck making the turn onto the westbound ramp. I caught her two miles later on the end of a run that lit every red light on my dashboard and poured steam from the grille. She looked at me without expression as I pulled alongside, then she coasted onto the shoulder. I parked behind her. Before I could turn it off, the Maverick murmured and died.

When I got to her window, she gave me a look that said, "What?"

"I just found Sonny in the bar at the Mesa," I said. Without saying anything, she reached into a bag on the passenger seat, handed the notebook through the window. I didn't take it. "Come to Chicago with me," I said.

She shook her head. "No," she said. "An hour ago... a year from now... maybe. But this... this is not the moment."

"I blew the moment," I said. "I know that. It scared me."

"I know," she said, wagging the torn, bloody notebook at me. " 'He came, he saw, he ran like a frightened animal' ...isn't that the way you put it?"

"...he came *back*," I added for her. "Then *she* ran...."

She nodded yes, tried to hand me the notebook again. When I didn't take it, she dropped it in the road and drove off.

I watched her out of sight, picked the notebook off the pavement, and walked to the smoldering Maverick. When I burned my hands trying to get the hood up, I thought, Forget it...just leave it where it is...it never would have made it to Chicago anyway.

It took a couple of trips to carry my duffel, two suitcases, a backpack, and the Olivetti through the spaces in the traffic, across the divider, and onto the eastbound shoulder. I wrote the word CHI big enough so that it just fit on a blank notebook page, held it against my chest, and put my thumb out.

A loaded cattle truck went by, kicked little dust devils out of the culvert with its slipstream, riffled the notebook, scattered half a dozen loose pages, hung them on the barbed-wire fence at the prairie edge of the ditch. As I was picking them off, I heard tires on the gravel behind me.

I folded the pages, closed them into the notebook, walked to the little truck, and leaned into the passenger window. "I'm going all the way to Chicago," I said. "I'm looking for one ride, straight through, so if you're turning off in Rock Springs or Green River or Cheyenne, I'd just as soon wait."

"Do I have to sign something?" she said, smiling that smile of hers. "Or why don't you just get in the truck and take your chances?"

Just at the eastern edge of town, we passed a crew-cab pickup with a bumper sticker that got us laughing so hard it felt like making love. PLEASE LORD, it said. LET THERE BE JUST ONE MORE OIL BOOM. THIS TIME I PROMISE I WON'T PISS IT ALL AWAY.